F R & Co
LEEDS

PLOUGHING ENGINES
IN FOCUS

by John Crawley

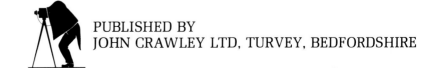

PUBLISHED BY
JOHN CRAWLEY LTD, TURVEY, BEDFORDSHIRE

©JOHN CRAWLEY LTD 1985

First published in 1985 by
John Crawley Limited
Field House, Turvey
Bedfordshire MK43 8DU

Printed in Great Britain by
AB Printers Limited, Leicester

ISBN 0 9508046 3 0

*The endpapers show a specially set up
official photograph taken circa 1860 showing
a two cylinder Kitson & Hewitson clip drum engine,
plough, rope porters and self moving anchor.*

FOREWORD

by David Scott
Chairman of the technical committee of
The Royal Agricultural Society of England

It is all too easy to dismiss the past, thinking it to be irrelevant in this modern age. We do this at our peril: our history is as important as our future; and for this reason John Crawley is to be congratulated for devoting so much time and energy to compiling a book which, with its wonderful collection of photographs depicting so clearly the development of steam ploughing engines and the special breed of men who devoted their lives to them, will rekindle the memory for those who like myself well remember seeing, as a child, the steam engines visiting the farm annually to carry out the ploughing ritual; and it will also excite the imagination of future generations who will always bless those who documented important milestones in the development of mechanical agriculture as we know it today. Without doubt the development of the steam plough was, like the invention of the combine harvester, a great milestone in the never-ending progression to achieve methods of husbandry which produce food at a price and in sufficient quantity to feed a hungry world.

The R.A.S.E. since its inception has striven to maintain its motto 'Practice with Science', and this has taken many forms, from livestock to agricultural machinery. Its works today embrace a far more complex industry than that envisaged at its foundation, but the principles remain the same, and in the field of agricultural machinery a great deal is done to help both farmers and manufacturers develop and utilize the latest technology.

Apart from the Royal Show, when a wide range of equipment is on static display, the Society puts on specialist working demonstrations covering a varied selection of enterprises such as irrigation, potato machinery, cultivation equipment, etc. There is also still in being the Machinery Award Scheme: this is a most comprehensive assessment of new and modified machinery which is inspected on farm and given awards, with the best receiving a silver medal and one outstanding machine each year receiving a gold medal.

In these and other ways the Society continues its tradition of encouraging the manufacture of new and better machinery.

However it is always nice and of great benefit to remember what has gone before, because, as in many industries, things often run a full circle, and old customs return to popularity. Ploughing and subsoiling are perhaps the most interesting current examples of this. Five years ago ploughs were being scrapped and direct drilling and minimal cultivation were all the rage: today plough sales have soared and with straw disposal a major problem is likely to remain a dominant feature of future cultivation techniques.

It is for that reason that it gives me great pleasure to write the foreword to this book, not only to remind us of our heritage but perhaps with current trends and the future of energy sources in doubt it will give inspiration to inventors and engineers in the future.

David Scott
16th April 1985

INTRODUCTION

From man's earliest days the cultivation of the soil has been one of his prime concerns. Primitive tools were supplemented or replaced by implements powered by horses or oxen, but as early as the year 1618 there was recorded a patent (No 6) for an invention to apply power other than that of animals to cultivation.

From that time onwards a succession of designs appeared: some were built, but many remained on paper — the unfulfilled dreams of their originators. Many years passed before, in 1852, John Fowler, founder of the well-known Leeds firm bearing his name, first introduced steam as the motive power for his drain plough.

Mr Fowler demonstrated the steam drain plough at the meeting of the Royal Agricultural Society of England at Lincoln in 1854, and the judges, after describing the performance and extolling the merits of the machine in their report, were led to say 'Surely this power can be applied to more general purposes. We earnestly recommend the idea to our engineers and machinists'.

Thus kindled, the fire of invention was soon fanned into flames, and from this period the steam engine would make the largest single contribution to the advancement of agriculture that the world had ever seen.

It is not the purpose of this book to examine the history of steam cultivation or to delve into technicalities, but a description of the systems used may help the uninitiated reader to understand the purposes for which the engines shown in these pages were built.

The Roundabout System of Steam Cultivation used a portable engine or a specially adapted traction engine which remained in one fixed position driving a windlass from which a wire rope was led round the field by pulleys so that an implement could be pulled backwards and forwards across the field. As the work progressed, the pulleys were moved back along the field towards the engine.

The Single Engine System of Steam Cultivation had the engine working up one headland, with a self-moving anchor winding itself up the opposite side of the field. The engine was fitted with a clipdrum on which the rope was gripped by clips to prevent slipping as it passed round the drum, across the field, and back round the anchor. The ends of the wire rope were attached to the implement fore and aft.

The Double Engine System of Steam Cultivation used two engines, one at each side of the field, simply winding the implement back and forth between them. While one engine was pulling, the other edged forward up the field by the working width of the implement, and the driver attended to his fire. By the time this was done, the implement would have reached the other engine, ready for the cycle to be repeated.

Direct Traction Steam Cultivation was tried by a number of firms, with the engine operating like a modern tractor, pulling or pushing an implement. The obvious disadvantages of this, as opposed to the other systems, were the high risk of getting set in muddy conditions, and the compaction of the soil caused by the great weight of the engine.

Of the many manufacturers of steam ploughing engines, the market leaders were certainly John Fowler & Co Ltd of Leeds. Photographs of Fowler equipment are therefore far more numerous than those of the products of other makers, a fact reflected by the contents of this volume.

As in my earlier books, machines in preservation are marked ■ after the engine number, and the building date given is usually that on which the engine became available to the sales department for collection or delivery.

To the many contributors of photographs, which are all individually acknowledged, I offer my sincere thanks; as also to the Road Locomotive Society (R.L.S.) for their kindness in allowing me to use the photographs taken by the late Major Ind. My thanks are also due to the Steam Plough Club for their help and for the loan of photographs; to David Phillips of the University of Reading Institute of Agricultural History and English Rural Life; and of course to Alan Duke for his unfailing support in helping to resolve the many queries that arose during the compilation of this book.

I am especially grateful to David Scott for his foreword, most appropriate since the Royal Agricultural Society of England was so closely involved in the development of the steam plough — staging trials, putting up large sums of money as prizes, and offering gold, silver and bronze medals to reward those who believed in the application of steam power to agriculture.

Had David Scott been alive in the early 1850s and performing the same honorary duties for the R.A.S.E. as he does today, then surely he would have been the chief advocate of steam ploughing.

John Crawley

LIST OF PLATES

Engine No.	Plate	Page
Aveling & Porter Ltd		
Rochester, Kent		
711	1	9
711	2	9
711	3	9
921	4	10
No details	5	10
1246	6	11
1248	7	11
1296	8	12
1304	9	12
1310	10	13
1311	11	13
1310 & 1311	12	14
1367	13	14
1512	14	15
1619	15	15
1677	16	16
1699	17	16
1873	18	17
1937	19	17
3370	20	18
4608	21	18
No details	22	19
4933	23	19
5658	24	20
5659	25	20
6283	26	21
6284	27	21
6818	28	22
7445	29	22
8053	30	23
8053	31	23
8137	32	24
8565	33	24
8890 ■	34	25
8890 ■	35	25
8891 ■	36	25
8954	37	26
8965	38	26
9147	39	27
Charles Burrell & Sons Ltd		
St Nicholas Works, Thetford		
No details	40	27
660	41	28
687	42	28
728	43	29
767	44	29
776 ■	45	30
777 ■	46	30
801	47	31
814	48	31
849	49	32
850	50	32
850	51	33
895	52	33
2890	53	34
Kitson & Hewitson		
Leeds		
Possibly 753	54	34
Balance cultivator	55	35

Engine No.	Plate	Page
Travelling anchor	56	35
No details	57	36
John Fowler & Co Ltd		
Steam Plough Works, Leeds, Yorkshire		
665 & 685	58	36
1053	59	37
1071	60	37
1188	61	38
1188	62	38
1225	63	39
1226	64	39
1332	65	40
1468 & 1469	66	40
1937	67	41
1938	68	41
2216	69	42
2457	70	42
No details	71	42
No details	72	43
No details	73	43
2602	74	43
2620 & 2621	75	44
2623	76	44
2623	77	44
2623 & 2687	78	45
2687	79	45
2687	80	45
2656 & 2825	81	46
2692	82	46
2861 ■	83	46
2927	84	47
3025	85	47
No details	86	48
3027 & 3028	87	48
3027 & 3028	88	48
3051	89	49
3052	90	49
3051 & 3052	91	49
No details	92	50
3064	93	50
3070 & 3071	94	51
3070 & 3071	95	51
3137	96	52
No details	97	52
3170	98	53
3170	99	53
3170 & 3173	100	53
3230	101	54
3230	102	54
3232	103	55
3251	104	55
3439 & 3440	105	56
3468	106	56
3496	107	57
3497	108	57
3532	109	58
No details	110	58
3548	111	59
3549	112	59
3550	113	60
No details	114	60
3958	115	60

Engine No.	Plate	Page
3616	116	61
3616	117	61
3617	118	62
3677	119	62
3721	120	63
3726	121	63
3835	122	64
3857	123	64
3887	124	65
3896	125	65
3958	126	66
4013	127	66
4386	128	67
4505	129	67
4657	130	68
No details	131	68
No details	132	69
No details	133	69
No details	134	70
No details	135	70
4680	136	71
4680	137	71
4740	138	72
No details	139	72
No details	140	73
No details	141	73
5378	142	74
6317	143	74
6518	144	75
6797	145	75
6992	146	76
7004	147	76
7071 & 7072	148	77
7071	149	77
7071	150	77
7225	151	78
7269	152	78
No details	153	78
7347	154	79
8203	155	79
No details	156	80
No details	157	80
No details	158	81
8204	159	82
8204	160	82
8204	161	82
8231	162	83
8232	163	83
8869	164	84
9077	165	84
9078	166	84
9265	167	85
9719	168	85
9733	169	86
9733	170	86
9754	171	87
9754	172	87
9896	173	88
10252	174	88
10316	175	89
10334	176	89
10403	177	90
10403	178	90

Engine No.	Plate	Page
10944	179	91
10944 & 10945	180	91
10945	181	91
11654	182	92
12242	183	92
12646	184	93
12647	185	93
12958	186	94
Implement	187	94
13400	188	94
13473	189	95
13474	190	95
13784	191	96
13794	192	96
13794 & 13795	193	96
13952	194	97
13956 & 13957	195	97
13983	196	97
Water cart	197	98
Sleeping van	198	98
14186	199	98
14269 ■	200	99
14269 ■	201	99
14270 & 14271	202	100
14273	203	100
14351 & 14352	204	101
14383 ■	205	101
14708	206	102
14708	207	102
14709	208	102
14727 ■	209	103
14734	210	103
15143 ■	211	103
15163 ■	212	104
15180	213	104
15192	214	104
15233	215	105
15418	216	105
15426 ■	217	105
15451 ■	218	106
15451 ■	219	106
16719	220	106
Plough	221	107
Plough	222	107
Plough	223	107
Windlass	244	117

Richard Garrett & Sons Ltd
Leiston, Suffolk

Engine No.	Plate	Page
32974	224	108
32974	225	108
33180	226	108

J & F Howard
Britannia Iron Works, Bedford

Engine No.	Plate	Page
	227	109
	228	109
	229	110
No details of	230	110
Howard engine	231	111
numbers have	232	111
survived	233	112
	234	113

Engine No.	Plate	Page
No details	235	113
No details	236	114
Manns Patent Steam Wagon Co		
Leeds		
No details	237	114
Marshall Sons & Co Ltd		
Gainsborough, Lincs		
6071	238	115
6071	239	115
J & H McLaren		
Midland Engine Works, Leeds		
15	251	120
112 ■	240	116
Plough	241	116
112 ■	242	116
112 ■	243	117
Fowler windlass	244	117
112 ■	245	117
1541 ■	246	118
1541 ■	247	118
1541 ■	248	118
1550	249	119
1551	250	119
1554 & 1555	252	120
Oxfordshire Steam Ploughing Company		
Cowley, Oxford		
No details	253	121
No details	254	121
41	255	122
56	256	122
73	257	123
73	258	123

Engine No.	Plate	Page
Ransomes, Sims & Jefferies Ltd		
Orwell Works, Ipswich, Suffolk		
14086	259	123
Savage Brothers Ltd		
St Nicholas Works, Kings Lynn		
No details	260	124
No details	261	124
No details	262	124
Savory & Son		
High Orchard Works, Gloucester		
No details	263	125
No details	264	125
Summerscales Ltd		
Phoenix Foundry, Keighley, Yorkshire		
No details	265	126
No details	266	126
Wallis & Steevens Ltd		
North Hants Iron Works, Basingstoke		
2854	267	127
2923	268	127
7327	269	128
Yarrow & Hilditch		
London		
No details	270	128

A Savage 'Agriculturist' engine at work on the Roundabout System.

1/2/3. Aveling & Porter 12nhp single cylinder ploughing engine No 711 was built in September 1871 and, with sister engine No 712, was sold to Chittenden, Knight & Co. Later both became the property of R.L. Knight & Co Ltd of Sittingbourne, Kent.
On 25th July 1905, whilst working at Rayham Farm on the Isle of Sheppey, she blew up with devastating results, killing her driver instantly.

(courtesy R.G. Pratt)

At the Board of Enquiry the evidence went to show that, of the thirty-one years of her life she had probably worked ten years, and it was coolly argued that she was therefore only ten years old. The Commissioners could not be persuaded to accept a theory more remarkable for its ingenuity than for its soundness. A short time before the accident a leak had started in the outside firebox, close to a bracket carrying some part of the gearing. A boilermaker was sent for but he had been unable to stop this leak and had returned to report to that effect. The engine commenced work and shortly afterwards blew up, scattering its fragments far and wide.

(author's collection)

(author's collection)

9

4.   Aveling & Porter 12nhp single cylinder ploughing engine, possibly No 921, built in April 1873 with sister engine No 922. These engines were sold to Wisbech Steam Cultivation & Threshing Company Ltd of Ely. Later they were sold to Jas. Wilderson of Elsworth, Cambridgeshire. This official photograph was taken outside the works at Rochester.   *(courtesy Institute Agricultural History)*

5.   Aveling & Porter 12nhp single cylinder ploughing engine which, although unidentified, was built between 1873 and 1876. Notable features are the vertical steering wheel and the wooden front axle-tree. On the smokebox is a plate proclaiming she was No 19 in the fleet. This picture was taken on 26th March 1923 when she was owned by Summers of York Road, London.   *(courtesy Major Ind/RLS)*

6.   Aveling & Porter 8nhp single cylinder ploughing engine, either No 1246, built in September 1876, or sister engine No 1277, built in December 1876. They were sold as a pair to Major General Sir Frederick W. Fitzwyoram of Havant, Hants. Sometime later they were acquired by William Wheatley of Wickham, Hants. In July 1916 they were sold to the Wingham Engineering Co. Ltd of Kent, their last recorded owner.

(courtesy Major Ind/RLS)

7.   Aveling & Porter 12nhp single cylinder ploughing engine No 1248, built in September 1876 with sister engine No 1247 and sold to L. Cooper and Company of Olney, Bucks. They are seen here on 28th September 1912 whilst the property of J.E. Pater of Olney who scrapped them in 1917.   *(courtesy Major Ind/RLS)*

8.   Aveling & Porter 8nhp single cylinder ploughing engine No 1296 was built in February 1877 with sister engine No 1297 and sold to the Earl of Dartmouth at Patshull, Staffordshire. Their next owner was Charles G. Sharpe & Sons of Donington, Lincs who worked them for an unspecified time before selling them to W. Dennis & Sons of Kirton, Lincs, where this photo was taken on 17th September 1915. In February 1918 they were sold to Walter Sharpe of Bicker, Lincs, where they stayed until scrapped in 1924.

(courtesy Major Ind/RLS)

9.   Aveling & Porter 8nhp single cylinder ploughing engine No 1304 which was built in March 1877 and, with sister engine No 1303, was fitted with two-speed ploughing gear. They were sold to Ballard & Eldrich of Brede, Sussex, later going to Arthur H. Cobbold of Claydon, Suffolk, who in turn sold them in 1903 to Arthur Dawson & Co (Rushmere) Ltd, Suffolk where they later received the Registration Nos BJ6007 and BJ6010. This photograph was taken on 20th October 1905 when with Arthur Dawson & Co.

(courtesy Major Ind/RLS)

10/11.   Aveling & Porter 8nhp single cylinder ploughing engines No's 1310 and 1311. Built in 1877 they were sold to Peter Smith of Bentworth, Hants and later they became the property of the Earl of Onslow of Clandon, Surrey. Their next owner was Arthur Cobbold of Claydon, Suffolk who sold them in 1903 to William Wilson of Darmsden Hall, Suffolk where during his ownership they received the Registration Nos BJ5808 and BJ5809. Engine No 1310 was scrapped in 1940 by E.J. Edwards: the fate of her sister is not recorded. Both photographs were taken at Darmsden Hall on 28th May 1918 and show No 1310 (above) and No 1311 (below).   *(courtesy Major Ind/RLS)*

13

12. Another photograph of the two 8nhp engines 1310 and 1311 shown on the previous page, and believed to have been taken at Baylam Mill, Suffolk. No 1311 is on the left and 1310 on the right. *(courtesy R.G. Pratt)*

13. Aveling & Porter 14nhp single cylinder ploughing engine No 1367 was built in August 1877 and sold to L. Cooper & Company of Olney, Bucks. Her next owner was E.A. Wing & Son of Walpole St Peter, Norfolk, where she spent the rest of her working life, seen here on 5th August 1913.   *(courtesy Major Ind/RLS)*

14.   Aveling & Porter 12nhp single cylinder ploughing engine No 1512, built in February 1880. With sister engine No 1511 they were sold to Jesse Ellice & Co of Maidstone, Kent, where they became Nos 11 and 12 in his fleet. They were advertised for sale on 1st October 1907 but the subsequent owner is not recorded.
(authors collection)

15.   Aveling & Porter Double cylinder ploughing engine No 1619 was built in July 1880. With sister engine No 1620 they were sold to the Emperor of Austria. *(author's collection)*

16.   Aveling & Porter 8nhp single cylinder ploughing engine No 1677 was built in 1881 with sister engine No 1676 for a customer in France, but for some reason they were not sent. In March 1892 they were sold to B. Field of Heaverham, Kent, later going to Thomas Hammond of Penshurst, Kent. Their last recorded owner was the Penshurst & Chiddingstone Agricultural Steam Company Ltd of Shoreham by Sea in Sussex where she was photographed on 16th July 1924.   *(courtesy Major Ind/RLS)*

17.   Aveling & Porter 16nhp double cylinder ploughing engine No 1699 was built in August 1881 with sister engine No 1700 and supplied to the order of Prince Kinsky. Further details are not recorded.

(courtesy Steam Plough Club)

18.   Aveling & Porter single cylinder ploughing engine No 1873, built in 1883 with sister engine No 1913.
They were not sold until October 1890 when they went to A.H. Clerke-Brown of Kingston Blount, Oxon
where they photographed on 21st September 1911. By May 1920 they had been given the Registration Nos
BH8363 and BH8362 and were owned by Avery Bros of Worminghall, Bucks.   *(courtesy Major Ind/RLS)*

19.   Aveling & Porter 16nhp single cylinder ploughing engine No 1937 was built in January 1884 with sister
engine No 1938. They were shipped to Brisbane for a customer in Australia.   *(author's collection)*

20.   Aveling & Porter 12nhp compound ploughing engine No 3370 was built in May 1894 with sister engine No 3371. They were sold to an owner in France.   *(author's collection)*

21.   Aveling & Porter 8nhp compound ploughing engine No 4608 was built in September 1900 with sister engine No 4607. They were the first engines of their type and were sold to L. Terry & Company of Offam, Kent where they remained for their working life. This photograph was taken on 18th July 1914.

(courtesy Major Ind/RLS)

22. This unidentified Aveling & Porter single cylinder chain driven ploughing engine was built prior to 1873, when gear drive and hornplates were introduced.   *(courtesy Steam Plough Club)*

23. Aveling & Porter 8nhp compound ploughing engine, either No 4933 or No 4934. Both were built in December 1901 and sold to G. & A.J. Keeble of Sealand, Cheshire. Later they were bought by G. & J. Ledson of Sealand, in whose ownership they were when this photograph was taken on 14th November 1917.

(courtesy Major Ind/RLS)

24. Either No 5658 or No 5659 photographed when owned by Hugh Kirkham on 20th September 1923.

(courtesy Major Ind/RLS)

Aveling & Porter 8nhp compound ploughing engines Nos 5658 and 5659 were built in January 1905 and sold to Charles Pickering of Pitsford, Northants. In 1914 they were bought by Frank Burgess of Stoke Bardolph, Norfolk, who sold them in August 1918 to Hugh Kirkham of Terrington St Clement, Norfolk, where they received the Registration Nos AH7488 and AH7489. They had a further two owners before being sold in 1932 to E.A. Wing & Son of Walpole St Peter, Norfolk who scrapped them in 1940.

25. The pair standing out of use at Walpole St. Peter.

(courtesy Steam Plough Club)

26. Official works photograph of No 6283 (author's collection)
Aveling & Porter 8nhp compound ploughing engines Nos 6283 and 6284, built in June 1907 and sold to Collick Son & Barham of Ivychurch, Kent. In 1917 they were bought by Fred Clark & Co. Ltd, of Ashford, Kent, in due time receiving the Registration Nos KE2627 and KE2628. Their next owners were R.H. Birch & Sons of Stanford, Kent. In 1931 they were advertised for sale and were bought by Thos. H. Gambrill of Petham, Kent, their last recorded owner.

27. No 6284 owned by Fred Clark & Co. Ltd on 11th September 1923. (courtesy Major Ind/RLS)

28.   Aveling & Porter 8nhp compound ploughing engine No 6818 built in July 1909 with sister engine No 6817 and sold to G.R. Le Grys of Heveningham, Suffolk. In 1919 they were sold to B.N. & C.E. Smith of Spalding where they received the Registration Nos DO1907 and DO1906. Their last owner was J.K. Gandy of Thurlby, Lincs. This photograph was taken at Spalding in 1932.   *(courtesy Steam Plough Club)*

29.   Aveling & Porter Class ZTD compound ploughing engine, either 7445 or 7446, *King George* or *Queen Mary*, was built in July 1911 and both were sold to Albert Price & Company of Blean, Kent. By August 1916 they had been bought by A. Kemsley of Aylesford, Kent where later they received the Registration Nos KR4257 and KR4258. Eventually they were sold to H.H. Naylor of Maidstone, Kent where they spent the rest of their working life, being seen here in Naylor's yard.   *(author's collection)*

30.   In the ownership of Wesley & Co Ltd.   *(courtesy Steam Plough Club)*

Aveling & Porter compound ploughing engine No 8053, built in July 1913 with sister engine No 8054 and sold to Wesley & Company Ltd, of Stretham, Ely where they received the Registration Nos EB243 and EB242. In 1924 they were sold to Sydney Smith of Stretham where they spent the rest of their working life.

31.   In the ownership of Sydney Smith.   *(courtesy R. Smith)*

32.   Aveling & Porter compound ploughing engine No 8137, built in December 1913 with sister engine No 8136 and sold to a customer in France. This official works photograph shows her on test prior to entering the point shop.   *(courtesy Aveling-Barford Ltd)*

33.   Aveling & Porter Class ZTD compound ploughing engine No 8565, built in April 1915. With sister engine No 8564 she was sold to William A. Kimpton of Somersham, Hunts, who worked them until August 1918 when he sold them to William Carley of Marshland Fen, Norfolk where they received the Registration Nos AH5782 and AH5781. By 1936 they had gone to Fred Darby & Sons of Sutton, Ely, their last recorded owner.   *(courtesy C. Roads)*

34. No 8890 at work.

Aveling & Porter Class ZTD Compound ploughing engines No 8890■ *Field Marshal Haig* and No 8891■ *General Byng.* Built in March 1918 and sold to Frank A. Cooke of Spalding where they received the Registration Nos DO1943 and DO1944. In 1936 they became the property of Chatterton & Cooke Ltd, of Tongue End, Lincs.
In February 1958 they were advertised for sale in *Farmer and Stockbreeder,* complete with three furrow deep plough, six furrow shallow plough, cultivator and living van. They were bought by R.E.P. Palmer of West Dereham, Norfolk who sold them on to G.T. Cushing of Thursford, Norfolk where they now feature in his museum.
(Courtesy Steam Plough Club)

35. 8890 on the road with the implements.

36. No 8891 bringing up the rear with the living van and watercart.

37.   Aveling & Porter Class ZTD compound ploughing engine No 8954 *Cleopatra*, Registration No NM267. Built in December 1918 with sister engine No 8955, *Hercules*, Registration No NM268, they were sold to Ralph Savage of Riseley, Beds where they spent all of their working life. This photograph was taken in their yard at Riseley in 1949.

(courtesy M.C. Fayers)

38.   Aveling & Porter Class ZTD compound ploughing engine No 8965, Registration No BL8304 was built in February 1919 with sister engine No 8966, Registration No BL8305 and sold to Jas. Baughan of Cholsey, Berkshire. By March 1928 they had been bought by A.H. & N. Bennett of Cuffley, Herts who sold them to Ernest W. Webb of Warboys, Hunts where they were last licenced in January 1937.

(courtesy C. Roads)

39.   Aveling & Porter Class ZTD compound ploughing engine, possibly No 9147 or 9148, in which case they were built in June 1920 and the photograph could have been taken on the Aveling & Porter stand at the Royal Show at Darlington in that year. If this surmise is correct they were sold to T.H. Ainsley of Burradon, Northumberland. In August 1922 they were sold to Wm G. Fairhead of Peldon, Essex where they received the Registration Nos NO6694 and NO6695. In June 1937 they went to their final home with J.D. Golding of Tolleshunt D'Arcey in Essex.   *(courtesy Aveling-Barford Ltd)*

40.   Burrell 10nhp ploughing engine with double cylinders and clip drum, built circa 1860 under licence from John Fowler of Leeds. This photograph was taken in the field adjoining St Mary's Abbey at the west end of Minstergate Street, Thetford.   *(courtesy Steam Plough Club)*

41.   Burrell 12nhp single cylinder long chain driven ploughing engine No 660 was built in June 1875 with sister engine No 659 and sold to Percy Everitt of Ryburgh, Norfolk. Their next owner was Tomeson of Wisbech, Ely who by July 1891 had sold them to Richard R. Holben of Burton, Cambs. Sometime later he sold No 660 on her own to Pamplin Bros of Cherry Hinton, Cambs where this photograph was taken on 25th June 1913.   *(courtesy Major Ind/RLS)*

42.   Burrell 12nhp single cylinder long chain driven ploughing engine No 687. Built in February 1875 with sister engine No 688, they were sold to C. Lambert of Sunk Island, Hull. They then had a succession of owners: Thomas Jaques of Brough, East Riding of Yorkshire; John W. Rix of Hingham, Norfolk where this photograph was taken on 19th June 1906 and Robert Blunt of Walpole Highway, Norfolk though the various dates are not recorded. Then circa 1911 to G.E. Hides of Brauncewell, Kesteven.   *(courtesy Major Inds/RLS)*

43.   Burrell 12nhp single cylinder short chain driven ploughing engine No 728 was built in May 1876 with sister engine No 729. They were sold to Martin Pate of Ely where in November 1897 they were reboilered and this photograph taken on 20th July 1911. Eventually they were sold to S.E. Covill of Ely where they received the Registration Nos EB3187 and EB3188. They were scrapped in 1938.   *(courtesy Major Inds/RLS)*

44.   Burrell 8nhp single cylinder gear driven ploughing engine No 767, built in November 1877 and exhibited at the Smithfield Show the following month. With sister engine No 775 built in April 1878 they were sold to Thomas O. Newman of Stansted, Essex in the same month. By September 1890 they had gone to Edward Green & Sons of North Walsham, Norfolk who in October 1902 sold them to John W. Rix of Hingham, Norfolk. By August 1904 they were with John W. Eagle of Walton on the Naze, Essex where they received the Registration Nos PU443 and PU444. Photographed on 3rd October 1925, they were eventually sold to T. Johnson of Ingham in West Suffolk, where they finished their working life. *(courtesy Major Ind/RLS))*

45/46. Burrell 8nhp single cylinder ploughing engine No 776■ (above) at Colchester on 17th October 1905 and No 777■ (below) just after repainting on 26th June 1906. Originally built in June 1879 and sold to Reginald G. Wilberforce J.P. of Woolavington, West Sussex, in July 1893 they went to C.W. Dorlin of Colchester, Essex, who eventually sold them to A. Borley of Colchester. Their next owners were the well known firm of engine dealers, George Thurlow & Sons of Stowmarket who it would seem took them in part exchange, later selling them to E. & W. Morley of Brize Norton, Oxon. When their working life was finished they were sold to R. Edwards of Swindon for scrapping where they languished for many years, becoming completely overgrown by brambles. Although badly rusted away the fact that they were thought to be the only surviving Burrell ploughing engines led to their purchase in 1966 for preservation. After two changes of ownership during which the restoration was undertaken they were sold to the Museum of East Anglian Life at Stowmarket where they are now on permanent exhibition.   *(both courtesy Major Inds/RLS)*

47. Burrell 14nhp single cylinder short chain driven ploughing engine No 801 was built in August 1878 and with sister engine No 802, was sold to W. Taylor of Hundon, West Suffolk. By February 1902 they had been bought by George Bedford of Little Bradley, West Suffolk and pictured there on 21st July 1911. When they were scrapped is not recorded but they were still at Little Bradley in 1915. *(courtesy Major Ind/RLS)*

48. Burrell 14nhp single cylinder gear driven ploughing engine No 814 was built in February 1879, sister engine No 815 being built the following month. They were sold to Thomas Clark of Chalford, Glos, where they received the Registration Nos DD2828 and DD2827 and were photographed on 10th June 1919. They finished up with Bomford Bros of Pitchill, Warks where they were scrapped in 1925. *(courtesy Major Ind/RLS)*

49. No 849 at Haverhill, 6th October 1921. (courtesy Major Ind/RLS)

Burrell 16nhp single cylinder ploughing engines Nos 849 and 850 were built in January 1881 and sold to Samuel F. Blackwell of Bideford on Avon, Worcs, but by August 1913 they had been bought by Bomford Bros of Pitchill, Warks. In 1916 they became the property of William Reynolds, engine dealers of Bedford, who sold them in January 1917 to Badcock & Reynolds of Haverhill, West Suffolk where they received the Registration Nos CF3889 and CF3890. In 1931 they went to Arthur Baldock of Haverhill and later No 850 was sold to C. Day of Smallford, Herts where she finished her days steaming greenhouses.

50. No 850 at Haverhill, 10th September 1919. (courtesy Major Ind/RLS)

51.   Burrell No 850 (see previous page) finishing her days steaming greenhouses at Smallford, Herts.

(author's collection)

52.   Burrell 10nhp single cylinder universal ploughing engine No 895 was built in March 1883 and sold to W.C. Cazalet of Grenehurst, Surrey with sister engine No 894 which was built in September of the previous year. By August 1891 they had gone to P. Everitt of East Molesey, Surrey. In 1893 they were taken back by Burrells, possibly in part exchange, and in the same year they were resold to Edward Mornement of Roudham, Norfolk. Later they became the property of Mornement & Ray Ltd, of East Harling, Norfolk. In 1910 they were sold to their last owners, Blyth & Squier of Stanford le Hope, Essex where this photograph was taken on 6th September 1919. *(courtesy Major Ind/RLS)*

53.   Burrell 16nhp single crank compound side drum ploughing engine No 2890, built in April 1907 with sister engine No 2889, they were sold to S. Flack of Orwell, Cambs where they received the Registration Nos CE8372 and CE8371. This shows her outside the Wheatsheaf public house on 3rd August 1912.

(courtesy Major Ind/RLS)

54.   Thought to be one of the batch of Kitson and Hewitson two cylinder 10nhp ploughing engines Nos 749-754, possibly No 753. Built circa 1860/3 these engines when built had three pulley ploughing gears, one under the hind tank, and the third on the forecarriage pin which also carried the pin for the winding forward drum. Most, possibly all, of these engines were altered and fitted with clip drum ploughing gear.

(courtesy W.W. Martin)

55. A fascinating scene showing the balance cultivator, with rope porters to keep the rope off the ground as much as possible to avoid excessive wear on the iron ropes, plus their attendant boys who's job it was to move them as the work progressed. Overseeing the operation is the landowner mounted on his trusty steed. Believed to have been photographed in the 1860s the clothing and headgear are worthy of note.

(courtesy W.W. Martin)

56. This is the travelling anchor which located the pulley on the opposite side of the field. As the implement travelled backwards and forwards between the anchor and the engine so it wound itself up the headland as the work proceeded. The knife-edged wheels biting into the land and the offset ballast box filled with heavy stones all helped to keep the anchor upright in resisting the pull of the implement rope round the pulley.

(courtesy W.W. Martin)

57.   Unidentified Kitson & Hewitson double cylinder slanting shaft ploughing engine. Built in 1862 under Fowler's patent she was fitted with Burton's clip drum, and became known as a slanting shaft engine because of the drive shaft which slanted from the crankshaft where it was driven through bevel gears to transmit the drive to the rear wheels. This machine was standing out of use on 15th February 1910 when owned by Pamplins of Cherry Hinton, Cambs.   *(courtesy Major Ind/RLS)*

58.   Fowler 10nhp single cylinder horizontal shaft ploughing engines Nos 665 and 685 were built in October 1868 and sold to the Rev. Thomas Stevens of Bradfield, Berks. On a date not recorded, ownership passed to Waller Bros of Rousham, Oxon. One of the pair was cut up in 1941. It is believed the other was purchased for preservation by a Mr Peter Hoseason but regretfully this too was cut up in 1945.

(S.P. Johnstone, courtesy R. Smith)

59. Fowler 10nhp single cylinder horizontal shaft ploughing engine No 1053. Built in September 1868 with sister engine No 1055 they were sold to Reuben Hunt of Halstead, Essex. Eventually they went to Edward Raven of Halstead where this photograph was taken on 9th October 1912. In December 1916 they were sold to R. Barrow of Buttermere, Wilts where they received the Registration Nos HR3386 and HR3385.

(courtesy Major Ind/RLS)

60. Fowler 10nhp single cylinder horizontal shaft ploughing engine No 1071 was built in September 1868 with sister engine No 1072, they were sold to Richardson & Ward of Maidenhed, Berks. By 1921 they were in the ownership of R.J. & H. Wilder of Wallingford, Berks having been given the Registration Nos BL3875 and BL4112. This photograph shows her in rebuilt form on 9th August 1933.   *(courtesy S.P. Johnston/R. Smith)*

61/62.   Fowler 12nhp single cylinder ploughing engine No 1188 was built in September 1869 with sister engine No 1187. They were sold to J.S. Davey of Redruth, Cornwall and later, on a date not recorded, they were resold to Fred Clark & Co Ltd of Ashford, Kent. By 1914 they were with E.J. Higgins of Oak Farm, Bonnington, Kent, where they received the Registration Nos KE4284 and KE4285. They then had a succession of owners, C. Loud of Ashford, Link Bros of Newchurch and finally Jarvis of Biddenden. The photograph above was taken in 1914 around the start of the war, hence the patriotic flying of the Union flag. The lower illustration is believed to have been taken in the thirties.   *(author's collection)*

63/64. In 1870 John Fowler & Co received an order for a pair of 12nhp double cylinder ploughing engines from John Alison of Reigate, Surrey which were to be built to his patented design. The main feature of this design was that the vertical winding drum was arranged to swivel so that a direct pull on the implement could be made, whatever the angle of travel of the engine on the headland. The engines were given the numbers 1225 (above) and 1226 (below) and were completed on 28th September 1870 and delivered through John Alison's Steam Ploughing Company to John Roynon of Chigwell, Essex. These two official works photographs show the differences between the two engines: the improved steering arrangement on 1226, a larger boiler, and a different layout of boiler fittings. *(author's collection)*

65.   Fowler 14nhp double cylinder ploughing engine No 1332, taken on 16th September 1915. Built in April 1870 with sister engine No 1329 they were sold to the Northumberland Steam Cultivating Company where they became their No 8 set. In January 1875 they went to Thomas Parkinson & Sons of East Ravendale, Lindsey where in February 1903 they received new Fowler boilers Nos 9576 and 9577. Later they were given the Registration Nos BE7961 and BE7962. In 1925 they were sold to A.W. Shepherdson of North Owersby, Lindsey. Their last owner was T. Stamp of Linwood, Lindsey.   *(courtesy Major Ind/RLS)*

66.   Fowler single cylinder ploughing engines Nos 1468 and 1469 were built in February 1871 and delivered to William Wood of Crockenhill, Kent through Ernest Beck of the Friends of the War Victims Fund. That same year they were taken to France to plough up the Franco-Prussian battlefields. In France the engines carried the slogan 'Society Agricole de France'. This photograph shows the two engines taking water from the pond at Orpington, Kent.   *(courtesy Thomas Wood & Sons Ltd)*

67/68. Fowler 14nhp single cylinder ploughing engines Nos 1937 (above) and 1938 (below) were built in 1873 and exported to Warsaw, Poland. Extra large fireboxes were fitted for straw burning on the Head & Schemioth system. The straw was fed into the firebox by powered rollers which were driven by belts direct from the crankshaft. In addition they were equipped to burn oil fuel as a means of increasing power or where the straw proved to be insufficient or wet.

At the time these engines were built front steerage was normal, but these were unusual in that the steersman was also the driver, all controls being mounted at the front end. This left the fireman free to attend to the fire and water which, on a rough road or field with unprotected belts and a moving straw table, was perhaps just as well. *(author's collection)*

69. Fowler 16nhp single cylinder ploughing engine probably No 2216 or 2217 wa built in September 1874 and sold to Shadrach Tompkins of Leckhampsted. They later wer to H.J. Drage of Chrishall, Essex and in March 1909 they were sold to A.W. Kimpton o Somersham, Hunts, and then in 1915 to Charles Taylor of Biggleswade, Beds. In June 1918 they became the propert of H.A. Christmas of Gransde Hunts where they received the Registration Nos EW2143 and EW2144. They were last licenced in 1928.
(author's collection)

70. Fowler 14nhp single cylinder ploughing engine No 2457 was built in January 1875 with sister engine No 2456. They were sold to J.H Hawkings of Ellenthorpe i the North Riding of Yorkshire This photograph of the ploughing gang was taken in Leicestershire in the twenties.
(author's collection)

71. An unknown Fowler single cylinder ploughing engine in a ditch at Barnham, Suffolk. The cause of this unfortunate accident was due to the breaking of the driving pin with the result that she ra away down a hill. The gentleman wearing the bowler hat is Harry Spencer, Burrell's erection shop foreman, talking with Bob Brundall, Burrell works driver.
(author's collection)

72/73. In May 1898
C.J. Goode of Elmdon, Suffolk
purchased a pair of 16nhp
single cylinder ploughing
engines Nos 2538 and 2539
from Ben Bomford of Pitchill,
Warwickshire. He found they
were very uneconomical on
coal and water and devised a
method of converting them to
compound cylinders. In 1903
he carried out his first
conversion on this pair of
engines, subsequently
converting four other pairs —
the last in 1918.
By lengthening the smokebox
he was able to fit the low
pressure cylinder in front of
the existing high pressure one
using a new long piston rod
carrying both pistons.
The number of the engine
shown in trouble in these two
photographs is not recorded
but the layout of the additional
cylinder is clearly seen.
(author's collection)

74. Fowler 14nhp single
cylinder ploughing engine
No 2602 was built in June 1875
together with sister engine
No 2605. They were sold to
C. Savage of Riseley, Beds who
used them on contract work
until 1918 when they were
sold to J. Hopkinson of Long
Bennington, Kesteven. Whilst
they were in his ownership
they received the Registration
Nos CT4266 and CT4267. By
August 1929 they had been
bought by R.P. Garland of
Oakring, Notts, the owner at
the time the photograph below
was taken.
(courtesy F.H. Gillford)

75. Fowler 12nhp single cylinder ploughing engines Nos 2620 and 2621, built in May 1875 and sold to Thomas Mobbs of Tadmarton, Oxon. They were later sold to and pictured with Thomas Jeffrey of Morton in the Marsh, Glos. Eventually No 2620 was sold to Thomas Wood & Sons of Crockenhill, Kent where she received the Registration No KE2322.
(courtesy R. Smith)

The following sequence of pictures show Fowler 12nhp single cylinder ploughing engines Nos 2623 and 2687, built in June 1875 and first sold to H. Harris of Longparish, Hants. Later they belonged to Terah F. Hooley of Papworth Everard, Cambs who named them *Papworth* and *Risley* and in 1908 No 2687 was reboiled by Fowells at St Ives, Hunts. In 1913 they were purchased by James Orchard of Leverstock Green, Herts, then in April 1943 they were advertised for sale, but as no other owner is recorded it is probable they were cut up around this time.

76. No 2623 *Papworth* at work near Hemel Hempstead.
(courtesy R. Smith)

77. No 2623 *Papworth* at work near Hemel Hempstead.
(courtesy R. Smith)

. No 2623 followed by 2687
epare to move to the next
b.
urtesy R. Smith)

9. No 2687 *Risley* in the
ackground as the work gets
nder way to splice the broken
ope.
courtesy R. Smith)

0. On left 2623 *Papworth* on
ight 2687 *Risley* at work
ultivating.
courtesy R. Smith)

81. Fowler 6nhp single cylinder ploughing engines Nos 2656 and 2825 were buil in August 1875 and November 1876 respectively. These two engines were only paired up when they became the proper of John Sutton of Southcote, Berkshire in August 1880. The owner's nameplate on th toolbox of No 2656 gives the name Jane Kinsey Sutton, Herefordshire which would seem to suggest that they stayed within the family but moved to a farm in Herefordshire.
Note how the photographer kept the village children back beyond the plough behind th second engine.
(courtesy R. Smith)

82. Fowler 12nhp single cylinder ploughing engine No 2692 was built in September 1875 with sister engine No 2693. They were sold to Charles Whatoff of Baston, Kesteven. Later they went to E. Hides of Great Chesterford, Essex, where the received the Registration Nos NO479 and NO480. In April 1916 they were given new Fowler boilers Nos 14591 and 14592. In 1935 they were bought by Charles R. Pumfrey & Sons of Duxford, Cambs wh two years later sold them to someone in the Sheffield area
(courtesy Major Ind/RLS)

83. Fowler 8nhp single cylinder ploughing engine No 2861■ was built in April 1876 with sister engine No 2862 and sold to John Cro of Taplow, Bucks. By 1901 they had been sold to R. & B. Bomford of Pitchill, and by 1921 No 2861■ had been sold on her own to J. Collins of Dormston, Worcestershire.
She was paired with No 3195 which Collins bought from Thomas Butler of Shinston, Worcestershire and they received the Registration Nos AB9451 and AB9452. This photograph, taken at Inkberrow, Worcester in August 1958, shows 2861■ with the chimney of 3195■ i the background overgrown with brambles.
(author's collection)

46

84.   Fowler 8nhp single cylinder ploughing engine No 2927 was built in July 1876 with sister engine No 2928. They were sold to W.D. Calvert of Sawbridgeworth, Herts. In April 1885 they were bought by John Robson & Sons of River, Kent, where this photograph was taken on 4th May 1927.   *(courtesy Major Ind/RLS)*

85.   Fowler 6nhp single cylinder ploughing engine either No 3025 or No 3026 was built in May 1877 and sold to F. Monkton of Tonbridge, Kent. They then had a succession of owners all in Kent: R.L. Knight of Sittingbourne, Wheatley Bros of Aldington and in 1915 Pickering & Higgins of Bonnington. The following year they went to their final home, Fred Clark of Ashford. She is illustrated on 27th July 1910 when owned by Wheatley Bros.   *(courtesy Major Ind/RLS)*

86. A Fowler 8nhp single cylinder convertible ploughing engine, the details of which are not recorded, photographed after running away down a hill and overturning at Whitney-on-Wye.
(courtesy R. Smith)

(courtesy R.G. Pratt)

87/88. Fowler 6nhp single cylinder ploughing engines Nos 3027 and 3028 were built in July 1877 and sold to William Levett of Cranbrook, Kent. In June 1913 they received new Fowler boilers Nos 13911 and 13912 and later the Registration Nos KE3629 and KE3628. In October 1922 they were sold to Baldwin Bros of Wadhurst, East Sussex where they spent the rest of their working life. The upper photograph was taken at Hill Farm, Cranbrook, and the one below at Wadhurst.

(courtesy C. Roads)

9. No 3051
photographed on
4th June 1913.
(Courtesy Major Ind/RLS)

Fowler 14nhp single
cylinder ploughing
engines Nos 3051 and
3052 was built in
September 1876 for Max
Smyth. In March 1883
they became the property
of A. England, of
Maldon, Essex who later
sold them to C.W. Dorlin
of Colchester. In 1904
they passed into the
ownership of
W.G. Fairhead of Peldon,
Essex. A new Fowler
boiler No 14459 was
supplied in April 1915
and fitted to No 3052.
Circa 1920 they received
registration Nos NO3113
and NO3114. In May
1923 No 3052 was
advertised for sale whilst
presumably No 3051 was
cut up for scrap.

10. No 3052
photographed on
4th June 1913.
(Courtesy Major Ind/RLS)

11. Nos 3051 and 3052
on the road at Ardleigh,
Essex on 30th March
1907.
(Courtesy Major Ind/RLS)

92. A Fowler single cylinder ploughing engine belonging to Eddison's of Dorchester in trouble at Puddletown, near Dorchester in 1914. The driver had backed up to the river to take water but went too near to the bank which gave way.

(courtesy R. Smith)

93. Fowler 14nhp single cylinder ploughing engine No 3064 pictured on 8th December 1916. Built in October 1876 with sister engine No 3063 for J. & A. Gadd of Clifton, Notts, by February 1922 they had been resold to Edward Waddington of Stoke Fields, Notts, where they received the Registration Nos NN2276 and NN2275. By October they were with R.P. Garland of Eakring, Notts, their last recorded owner.

(courtesy F.H. Gillford))

94/95. Fowler 14nhp single cylinder ploughing engines Nos 3070 and 3071 were built in September 1876. They were sold to Greig of Fareham, related to David Greig of Fowler's and were specially made with steel gears throughout. In December 1910 they were sold to J.C. Richardson Ltd of Fareham, where they received the Registration Nos HO5843 and HO5844. In 1937 the firm closed down and they were pictured in steam at the sale on 15th July when sold for £35 the pair to F.W. Pound of Portchester where they were scrapped in 1950.

(courtesy S.P. Johnstone/R. Smith)

96.   Fowler 8nhp single cylinder ploughing engine No 3137 was built in May 1877 and with sister engine No 3134 they were sold to Henry Vamplew of Grimoldby, Lindsey. Later they went to Terah F. Hooley of Papworth Everard, Cambs. In March 1911 they were sold to T. Fuller of Lewes, East Sussex where they received the Registration Nos AP9111 and AP9113. This photograph was taken on 10th August 1918.

(courtesy Major Ind/RLS)

97.   A Fowler 14nhp single cylinder ploughing engine at work on land reclamation on the Duke of Sutherlands estate near Loch Shin, Scotland. One of the principal objects which the Duke of Sutherland had in view in reclaiming waste land was to provide winter feed for sheep. In *The Times* of 7th December, 1880 it was recorded that sheep from the newly reclaimed land of Sutherland are the best Scotch mutton on the market and have fetched a price which has not been touched by any of the others *viz.* 8½d (.035p) per lb (.454 kilos). The special plough being used in this operation was designed and patented by the Duke. At each end was a large hook-like tine which travelled in the ground behind the plough to a depth of 30 inches loosening any large stones or boulders in its path.

(author's collection)

98/99/100. Fowler 12nhp single cylinder ploughing engines Nos 3170 and 3173 were built in May 1877 and sold to Thomas Garley of Orlingbury, Northants. By 1893 they were with F.W. Dickens of Whelpley Hill, Bucks, their last recorded owner and where these photographs were taken. (courtesy R. Smith)

101.   Foreman Bert Gardener on the engine whilst dredging the lake in Fairford Park for Huntley & Palmer about 1927.
(courtesy Institute Agricultural History)

Fowler 8nhp single cylinder ploughing engine No 3230 was built in July 1877 with sister engine No 3229. They were sold to Ben Bomford of Pitchill, Warwickshire. In 1904 they became the property of Bomford & Evershed of Salford Priors, Warwickshire and were still in their ownership in 1948, during which time they received the Registration Nos AC9065 and AC9064.

102.   Pulling out trees sometime in the nineteen-thirties.
(courtesy Institue Agricultural History)

103.   Fowler 8nhp single cylinder ploughing engine No 3232 was built in July 1877 and sold to Thomas Wood & Sons of Crockenhill, Kent, where she spent the whole of her working life, eventually receiving the Registration No KE2320. In 1913 she was converted to a compound engine by fitting a Burrell single crank compound cylinder block and in 1927 she received a new firebox by Aveling & Porter. Last used in 1935 she was scrapped in 1936.   *(courtesy Thomas Wood & Sons Ltd)*

104.   Fowler 14nhp single cylinder ploughing engine No 3251 was built in August 1877 with sister engine No 3252 and sold to H. Yates & Co of Grantham. She was later sold to Thomas Jeffrey at Moreton in Marsh, Glos. In June 1887 she was sold to her last owner R.H. Hurst whose address is not recorded. *(courtesy R. Smith)*

105. Fowler 8nhp single cylinder ploughing engines Nos 3439 and 3440 were built in August 1878 and sold to W. Burrows of Boseley, Worcestershire. By 1921 they were owned by Bomford Bros of Pitchill, Warwickshire and carried the Registration Nos AC9593 and AC9596. Later they were sold to Blackwell & Son of Northampton, their last recorded owner.   *(courtesy C. Roads)*

106. Fowler 16nhp single cylinder ploughing engine No 3468 was built in July 1878 with sister engine No 3472. They were sold to Dean & Adamson of Cottenham, Cambs and in 1919 they went to James Jackson & Sons of Sawtry, Hunts, where they received the Registration Nos EW2505 and EW2506. In 1931 they were sold to Swales, Cole & Beaver of Coppingford, Hunts their final home. This photograph taken in 1925 clearly shows the circular cover on the cylinder block which discloses that the engine was fitted with the Church valve.   *(courtesy Major Ind/RLS)*

107/108. Fowler 14nhp single cylinder ploughing engines Nos 3496 and 3497 were built in May 1878 for L. Barnard & Co of Petersfield, Hants. Eventually they passed into the ownership of Ben Howkins of Bromham, Beds, who later sold them to William Reynolds of Bedford. In December 1917 they were purchased by Charles Cherrington of Hadleigh, West Suffolk, where they were fitted with Burrell single crank compound cylinder blocks and received Registration Nos CF3461 and CF3462. In 1939 they went to J.H. Kemble of Hadleigh who sold them in 1942 to Frank Sainsbury of Little Wratting, West Suffolk, where they stayed until 1947 when it is believed they were cut up.

The photograph above was taken at Bildeston in June 1935 and the lower one at Hadleigh.

(courtesy R.G. Pratt)

109.   Fowler 14nhp single cylinder ploughing engine No 3532 was built in July 1878 with sister engine
NO 3531 and sold to Joseph Unwin of Coggeshall, Essex. They later went to Smith & Willsher, also of
Coggeshall, where this photograph was taken on 28th September 1905. In 1914 they were sold to S.W. Blyth
of Ingatestone, Essex where they stayed until they were scrapped.   *(courtesy Major Ind/RLS)*

110.   A pair of Fowler 14nhp single cylinder ploughing engines belonging to R. & B. Bomford of Pitchill,
Warwickshire in a specially posed photograph, showing driver George Batchelor on the front engine with
driver John Brookes on the rear engine and H. Bennett on the plough.   *(courtesy R. Smith))*

111/112. Fowler 16nhp single cylinder ploughing engines Nos 3548 (above) and 3549 (below) fitted with Church valves they were built in February 1879 and sold to Charles Tomenson of Sleaford, Lincs. By 1921 they were with William Thompson & Sons of Upwood, Hunts, where they received the Registration Nos EW2466 and EW2467. By 1927 they were with their last owner, M.E. Yeomans of Upton, Hunts where these photographs were taken on 15th May 1923. *(courtesy Major Ind/RLS)*

113. This Fowler 16nhp single cylinder ploughing engine fitted with Church val is either No 3550 or 3551 and was built in March 1879 and sold to S. Roberts & Co of Coates, Glos. They were later sold to H.W. Kirby of Maldon Essex, then, circa 1918, to Henry Goode of Elmdon who converted them to compound In December 1918 they were bought by William Reynolds, dealer of Bedford, who sold them to Noah T. Hull, also of Bedford, where they received the Registration Nos NM115 and NM116. In 1923 they wer purchased by E. Deamer of Bourn, Cambs.
(author's collection)

114. An unidentified pair of Fowler-Goode compound ploughing engines on the roa
(courtesy R.G. Pratt)

115. Fowler 8nhp single cylinder ploughing engine No 3958 was built in July 188 and with sister engine No 393 (built in August of the same year) sold to Godden & Samso of Lydd, Kent. They were late sold to W. Blacklocks, also of Lydd, before going to William Reynolds of Bedford. They were bought by E.J. Goode wh converted them to compound and sold them in December 1918 to W. Goode of Chrishal Essex. Some years later they became the property of Harry Flack, also of Chrishall. By 1946 No 3938 had been acquired by C.J. Budd of Nazeing, Essex and by 1948 No 3958 had gone to J. Pritchard of Chingford, Essex. It is believed that both engine finished their days with these owners sterilising soil. They were the last pair to be converted by Goode before the firm was sold by auction on 18th December 1918.
(author's collection)

(courtesy R.G. Pratt)

116/117.   Fowler 16nhp single cylinder ploughing engine fitted with Church valve No 3616 was built in May 1879 with sister engine No 3624. They were sold to Eastchurch Steam Plough Company in Kent where they worked until 1897 when they were sold to Pamplin Bros of Cherry Hinton, Cambs. In 1904 No 3616 blew up with disastrous results but the following year was rebuilt receiving a new Fowler boiler No 10305. They later received the Registration Nos CE7701 and CE7702. These photographs were taken at the scene of the accident at Linton in 1904 by 'Francis' a professional photographer of Saffron Walden.

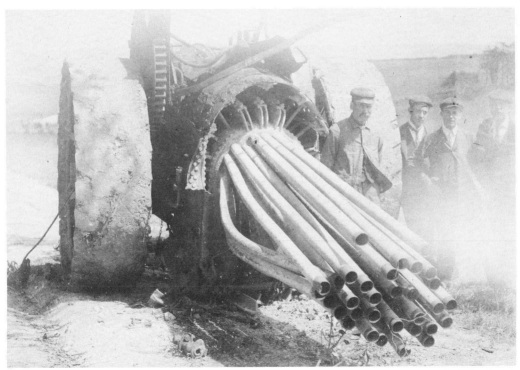

(author's collection)

118.	Fowler 16nhp single cylinder ploughing engine No 3617 was built in March 1879 with sister engine No 3615. They were sold to Albion Andrews of Ilchester, Somerset and later went to Lord Portman of Orchard Portman, Dorset. Next they came into the ownership of William Reynolds of Bedford who by July 1908 had sold them to J. & S. Hinsby of St. Neots, Hunts where this photograph was taken on 20th April 1912. They next went to Dynes & Son of Kempston, Beds where they received the Registration Nos NM1089 and NM1088. By 1923 they were back with J.&.S. Hinsby who, by 1926, had sold them to M.B. Sutherland of Ravensden, Beds. In 1928 they were back with Reynolds who presumably scrapped them.

(courtesy Major Ind/RLS)

119.	Fowler 8nhp single cylinder ploughing engine No 3677 was built in September 1879 as a single engine and sold to John Brown of Ancroft, Northumberland. Her next owner was J. Black & Sons of Notham-on-Tweed, Northumberland who in October 1896 returned her to Fowlers. In August 1898 she was purchased by Joseph Baxendale of Hursley Park, Hants who paired her up with Fowler No 2860 of 1876 and sold them to C. Holloway of Itchen Abbas, Hants. They were later acquired by Sir John Shelley-Rolls, Bart, of Alvington Park, Hants, where this photograph was taken on 27th April 1918, where they received the Registration Nos HO5649 and HO5650 and spent the rest of their working life.	*(courtesy Major Ind/RLS)*

120.   Fowler 16nhp single cylinder ploughing engine No 3721 was built in July 1879 with sister engine No 3725. They were sold to the Eastchurch Steam Ploughing Co Ltd, Kent. By 7th May 1915 she had been sold on her own to J.W. Ward of Withcall, Lindsey, who later sold her to E.A. Foley of Bourne where she was advertised for sale in 1921.   *(courtesy Major Ind/RLS)*

121.   An unidentified Fowler 16nhp single cylinder ploughing engine, either No 3726 or 3728. These were built in 1879/1880 and sold to R.B. Tetley of Great Baddow, Essex. By 22nd July 1904, when this was taken, they were in the ownership of M. & W. Spooner of Great Baddow. In November 1910 No 3726 was fitted with a new Fowler boiler No 12689 followed in December 1911 with No 3728 receiving boiler No 13179. Eventually they were given the Registration Nos NO922 and NO921.   *(courtesy Major Ind/RLS)*

122. Fowler 14nhp single cylinder ploughing engine No 3835 was built in May 1880 with sister engine No 3836 and sold to Marshland Steam Cultivating Company, near Goole, West Riding. By February 1910 they had been sold to A.J. Ward & Sons of Egham, Surrey. In 1912 No 3835 (and perhaps No 3836) was rebuilt by A.J. Ward & Sons and fitted with a cylinder block and safety valves supplied by the Oxford steam ploughing company and given the name *Shamrock* (as shown above). They later received the Registration Nos PB9666 and PB9667 although these were subsequently changed to PB9669 and PB9670. They were last licenced in December 1944. *(author's collection)*

123. Fowler 8nhp single cylinder ploughing engine No 3857 was built in July 1880 with sister engine No 3858 for Major W.R.M. Thoyts of Sulhampstead, Berks. By 1921 they had been sold to the Wingham Engineering Company Ltd, Kent, where they received Registration Nos KE3177 and KE3178 and where this photograph was taken in September 1926. No 3858 was later sold to George Taylor of Redbourn, Herts.

(courtesy Major Ind/RLS)

124. Fowler 8nhp single cylinder ploughing engine No 3887 was built in September 1880 with sister engine No 3889. They were sold to William Thompson of Thurleigh, Beds, where they spent their working life. By 4th August 1927, when photographed, they were owned by the engine and scrap dealer George Taylor of Redbourn, Herts. *(courtesy Major Ind/RLS)*

125. Fowler 8nhp single cylinder double drum ploughing engine No 3896, fitted with Church valve, was built in September 1880 and sold to T.M. Cleasby of Wilton Grange, Wiltshire. In March 1894 she was sold to J. & H. Tovey of Cirencester, Glos, where she was paired with Fowler No 4223■. In the early twenties they were bought by Bomford & Evershed of Salford Priors, Warwickshire, receiving the Registeration Nos AC9062 and AC9061. No 3896 was sold for scrap in 1961, her mate going into preservation. The photograph shows the side tanks fitted to carry the water as the second drum was beneath the tender.

(courtesy Institute Agricultural History)

126.   Fowler 8nhp single cylinder ploughing engine No 3958 fitted with Achilles valve. Built in August 1881 she was paired with No 3938 which was fitted with an ordinary valve and built in July 1881. They were sold to Godden & Samson of Lydd, Kent where this photograph was taken on 19th July 1907. They then went to William Reynolds of Bedford who sold them to E.J. Goode of Elmdon, Essex, where they were converted to tandem compounds on the Goode system. By December 1918 they were with W. Goode of Chrishall, Essex where they received the Registration Nos NO129 and NO127. Their next owner was Harry Flack of Chrishall but by 1946 he had sold them to C.J. Budd of Nazing, Essex. By 1948 No 3958 had gone to J. Pritchard of Chingford, Essex for sterilising soil.   *(courtesy Major Ind/RLS)*

127.   Fowler 6nhp single cylinder ploughing engine No 4013 was built in August 1882 with sister engine No 4012.and sold to Grimwood Cooke of Linton, Cambs. Their next owner was J.P. Charter of Comberton, Cambs although the date of sale is not recorded. In August 1914 he sold them to M. Radford of Barton, Cambs where this was taken on 31st March 1921.   *(courtesy Major Ind/RLS)*

128. Fowler Class Z compound ploughing engine No 4386 was built in 1882 and delivered to the Magdeburg Branch for a customer in Germany. The two-speed, two-shaft ploughing gear and the vertical tank steering are points worthy of note in this works photograph. *(author's collection)*

129. Fowler 10nhp compound ploughing engine No 4505 was built in March 1883 with sister engine No 4504. Sold to Holborow & Co of Dudbridge, Glos, they were later purchased by S. Blackwell of Bickmarsh, Worcs. In 1912 they were sold to Bomford & Evershed of Salford Priors, but in 1917 they became the property of Bomford Bros of Pitchill. By 1921 they were owned by B. Bomford & Co of Harvington, Worcs and received the Registration Nos NP41 and NP40. They survived until 1943 but the date of scrapping is not recorded. This shows No 4505 working for the War Dept on Salisbury Plain during the First World War hauling material on sledges in winter when the mud made horse haulage impossible. *(courtesy R. Smith)*

130.   Fowler 16nhp single cylinder ploughing engine No 4657 was built in January 1884 together with sister engine No 4656. They were sold to G.T. Morcroft of Westwood Park, Southampton. By 28th August 1919, when this was taken, they were owned by Watson & Haig of Andover, receiving the Registration Nos HO6089 and HO6090.   *(courtesy Major Ind/RLS)*

131.   An unknown Fowler ploughing engine belonging to Bomford & Evershed of Salford Priors, Warwickshire photographed circa 1930 dredging Coutharth Park, Sunningdale for Lord Derby. Foreman Bert Bloxham is on the extreme left.   *(courtesy Institute Agricultural History)*

132/133. Two fascinating photographs of a pair of unidentified Fowler 12 or 14nhp single cylinder ploughing engines taken circa 1920. They have left hand cylinders and are fitted with long smokeboxes with what appears to be some form of damper control mounted on the front. *(courtesy F.H. Gillford)*

134/135. Two more unidentified Fowler single cylinder ploughing engines, either 12 or 14nhp. The upper picture shows an engine fitted with a form of modified safety valve whilst the lower one shows an engine fitted with the safety valves supplied by the Oxford Steam Plough company. *(courtesy F.H. Gillford)*

136. In Bomford & Evershed's yard, 18th July 1923. (courtesy Major Ind/RLS)

Fowler 10nhp single cylinder ploughing engine No 4680, built in April 1884 and sold with sister engine No 4681 to John Webster of Barnston, Cheshire. In July 1898 they were sold to a Mr. R. Chatterton who worked them for nearly sixteen years before selling them in 1914 to Bomford & Evershed of Salford Priors. Here they were reboiled, receiving boilers 14369 and 13193, and also Registration Nos AC9066 and AC9067. In 1956 they became the property of Bomford & Carr, later Bomford & Wilkins Ltd, both of Binton, Warwickshire. Finally they suffered the ultimate indignity of being fitted with diesel engines.

137. At work around 1930. (courtesy Institute Agricultural History)

138. Fowler 16nhp compound ploughing engine, one of the pair No 4740 and No 4741, built in July 1886 for the Earl of Westmorland of Apethorpe, Northants. Later they went to Sir H. Brassey, also of Apethorpe in whose ownership they were given the Registration Nos BD5403 and BD5402 and this one was photographed on 8th October 1926. Their next owner was L.F. Briggs of Stamford, followed by Jeremiah Carley of Chatteris, Ely, before finally going to Joseph Swales of Corpusty in Norfolk where they were last licenced in 1930.   *(courtesy Major Ind/RLS)*

139. A pair of Fowler single cylinder ploughing engines as rebuilt by John Allen & Sons (Oxford) Ltd. The cast iron chimneys and 'Oxford' pattern safety valves are distinctive features of this firm's rebuilding. The engines are believed to be a set belonging to Beeby Bros of Rempstone and are thought to be taking water on the outskirts of Nottingham in the thirties.   *(courtesy F.H. Gillford)*

140/141.   An unknown Fowler single cylinder ploughing engine after having run away down East Hill in Dartford. The *Dartford Chronicle* of Saturday 3rd June 1882 stated 'as a traction engine, belonging to Mr Thomas Wood, Crockenhill, was coming down East Hill, Dartford, drawing a truck of bricks from Fawkham to the site of the new Congregational Church, West Hill, Dartford, which is being erected by Naylor of Rochester, two studs connected with the main driving shaft broke and the huge iron horse descended the hill at terrific speed, much to the danger of the residents and wayfarers at the time. The driver told the stoker to jump off, but he himself courageously kept to his post at the engine until it was brought to a standstill. In falling over the parapet the engine went clean over a boy named Atkins, but he, most miraculously, was uninjured. The only serious casualty was the grand-daughter of Mrs Newman from next door who suffered a broken left leg.'

These photographs showing driver Thomas Holmwood and his stoker posing on their engine were taken by W. Owen of Bexleyheath on 2nd June 1882. *(courtesy Thomas Wood & Sons Ltd)*

142.   Fowler 8nhp compound ploughing engine No 5378 was built in February 1887 with sister engine No 5379. They were sold to William Woods of Warnford, Hants where they spent their working life, during which time they received Registration Nos HO6168 and HO6169. This photograph was taken on 31st May 1909.   *(courtesy Major Ind/RLS)*

143.   Fowler 16nhp single cylinder ploughing engine No 6317 was built in 1890 with sister engine No 6316 and delivered to the Magdeburg branch in Germany. Note the hand vice fitted to the rear of the tender, a most useful addition to any engine.   *(author's collection)*

144.   Fowler 6nhp compound ploughing engine No 6518, built in October 1892 with sister engine No 6519 and sold to F.L. Cobb of Sheldwick in Kent. In May 1895 they were bought by Holman Bros of Canterbury, Kent where they received the Registration Nos FN5023 and FN5022 and where this picture was taken on 14th September 1925. They were last licenced in 1937.   *(courtesy Major Ind/RLS)*

145.   Fowler 16nhp single cylinder ploughing engine No 6797 was built in January 1896 with sister engine No 6800. They were sold to Samuel W. Farmer of Little Bedwyn, Wiltshire. They were later sold via the Oxford Steam Ploughing Company to Frank Stratton of Alton Priors, Wilts where this photograph was taken on 9th July 1919.   *(courtesy Major Ind/RLS)*

146. Fowler Class A3 compound traction engine No 6992 fitted with ploughing gear was built in July 1893 as a single engine and sold to a customer in Piedmont, Italy. This works photograph shows her undergoing steam trials before entry into the paint shop.   *(author's collection)*

147. Fowler Class T1 single cylinder ploughing engine No 7004 was built in 1894 and delivered to the Magdeburg branch for a customer in Germany. This type of engine was intended for the single engine system of ploughing, working along the side of the field opposite to the moving anchor. To enable the engine to undertake other jobs on the farm the winding gear could be removed and carried on a special trolley constructed for that purpose.   *(author's collection)*

...wler Class K3 single cylinder
...ughing engine No 7071 was
...lt in September 1894 with
...er engine No 7072 and sold
...W. Champion of
...dlesworth, Norfolk. In July
...3 they went to Sturgeon
...s of Stanton in West Suffolk
...o worked them for nearly
... years before selling them in
...y 1913 to Robert Nesling of
...field, East Suffolk where
...y received the Registration
...s BJ6815 and BJ6816. They
...re last licenced in 1928.

... An early view of
...s 7071 and 7072 on
... road.

...rtesy R.G. Pratt)

... Seen here on
...h August 1924...

...rtesy Major Ind/RLS)

...0. ...and 6th October 1925.

...urtesy Major Ind/RLS)

151. Fowler Class K5 single cylinder ploughing engine No 7225, built in 1895 with sister engine No 7224 and delivered to the Magdeburg Branch in Germany. These engines had removeable winding drums which enabled them to undertake other work about the farm.
(author's collection)

152. Fowler Class A4 'Farmers Engine' No 7269 was built in October 1894 and sold to John Barclay of Harrieston, Kincardineshire. By November 1924 she was in the ownership of Alexander Barron of Lawrence Kirk, Kincardineshire.
This works photograph shows the first of the class which was basically the A4 traction engine fitted with ploughing gear.
(author's collection)

153. This photograph was received by Fowlers on 15th November 1905 from R. Mansbridge of the Honolulu Plant Company and shows a compound Fowler ploughing engine working with a bush destroyer on the Oahu Sugar Company Estate.
(courtesy Institute Agricultural History)

154.   Fowler Class AA2 single cylinder ploughing engine No 7347 was built in June 1895 and sold with sister engine No 7348 to Burton upon Trent Corporation for use on their sewerage farm. In due course they received the Registration Nos FA1027 and FA1028. In 1931 the sister engine was considered beyond economical repair and was scrapped, but 7347 survived until 1951. This photograph was taken on the Burton sewerage farm on 8th September 1905. *(courtesy Major Ind/RLS)*

155.   Fowler Class T1 double drum single cylinder ploughing engine No 8203 was built in January 1899 and sold to Birmingham Tame, Rea & District Drainage Board where she received the Registration No OL3343. In 1928 she was sold to Bomford & Evershed of Salford Priors, Warks, where she spent the rest of her working life. *(courtesy Institute of Agricultural History)*

156/157/158. Fowler 14nhp single cylinder ploughing engine belonging to Beeby Bros, steam ploughing contractors of Rempstone, Notts in trouble on the Ashby Folville to Gaddesby road (today the B674) circa 1905. The bridge had been rebuilt around 1904 and opened for light traffic only and then, some twelve months later, after inspection by the County Highways Engineer it was declared fit for all traffic. Within three days of the bridge being opened for heavy vehicles Beeby Bros had occasion to cross over it with a pair of their engines and tackle. The first engine drawing the plough passed over without trouble but the second engine caused the bridge to collapse, dropping the back of the engine to the level of the stream and the living van it was towing to drop forward onto the tender of the engine. The steersman jumped free but the driver was trapped in the tender and had to smash his way through the front of the van in order to escape as can be seen in the photograph above. Later the first engine unhitched the plough and by a roundabout route of backroads came up behind the accident and was able to draw the van back up onto the road, couple up and return to its original position. Meanwhile a gang of men had been digging out the road to provide an incline up which the damaged engine could be hauled back onto the road. *(courtesy Beeby Bros)*

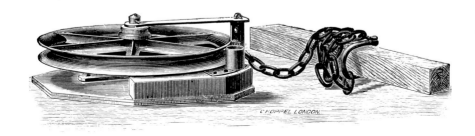

159/160/161. Fowler Class ?
single cylinder ploughing
engine No 8204 was built in
February 1899 and sold to
Captain E.W. Baird of Exning
Suffolk. Later she came into
the hands of dealer William
Reynolds of Bedford who sol
her in January 1916 to Hugh
Kirkham of Terrington St.
Clements, Norfolk. In
November 1918 she was bou
by F. Smith of Cavendish,
West Suffolk who later sold
to Walter F. Bear of Acton, a
in West Suffolk. She was sti
in his ownership when the
author took these photograph
of the derelict engine at a
gravel pit near Long Melford
March 1956. The centre pictu
shows the double cable drum
in detail.
(author's collection)

162. No 8231 at work on 16th June 1927 when owned by A. Thomas Loyd. (courtesy Major Ind/RLS)

Fowler Class B4 side drum compound ploughing engines Nos 8231 and 8232 were built in April 1899 and sold to Lady Wantage of Lockinge, Berks. They later became the property of A. Thomas Loyd, also of Lockinge and then of A.J. Hosier of Wexcombe, Wilts before being sold to R. Edwards of Swindon.

163. No 8232 lying derelict in Edwards yard at Swindon in 1957. (author's collection)

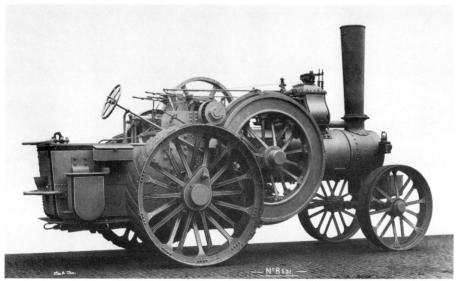

164. Fowler Class B4 side drum compound ploughing engine No 8869 was built cir 1904 with sister engine No 8868. They were delivered to the Magdeburg Branch for customer in Germany.
(author's collection)

Fowler Class K5 single cylind ploughing engines No's 9077 and 9078 were built in September 1901 and sold to Nottingham Corporation, whe they spent all of their workin lives. They received the Registration Nos AL9294 and AL9295 and were eventually scrapped in 1933.

165. No 9077 at Stoke Bardolph, Notts in 1916.
(courtesy F.H. Gillford)

166. No 9078 at work on 11th November 1922.
(courtesy Major Ind/RLS)

167.   This photograph of a Fowler Class AA2 compound ploughing engine, either No 9265 or 9266, was taken on 23rd March 1902 shortly after they were built and sold to Daniel Congdon of Bishop's Stortford, Herts. Their next owner was C. Rayment, also of Bishop's Stortford, and then, on a date not recorded, they were sold to Pamplin Bros of Stansted in Essex during which time they received the Registration Nos NK1261 and NK1260.   *(courtesy Major Ind/RLS)*

168.   A Fowler Class K5 compound ploughing engine either No 9719 or 9720, both built in January 1904. The late Alf Pepper of Fowlers was involved with the building of these engines which were a special order for the Caroni Sugar Estates in Trinidad and were fitted with extended smokeboxes and front mounted jib cranes. He sailed with them on the S.S. *Napernia* on 30th November 1904 along with B4 ploughing engines Nos 10211 and 10212.   *(courtesy Institute of Agricultural History)*

169/170. Fowler Class D2 single cylinder traction engine No 9733 was built in 1908. She was fitted for direct traction ploughing and sold to a customer in Rhodesia. It is recorded that she was converted to a compound engine but it is not known if this was done before she was sent abroad. These two works photographs show her on test with four-furrow AB plough No 619 (above) and (below) with seven-tine cultivator No 6879.

(courtesy Institute of Agricultural History)

171/172. Fowler Class AA2 compound ploughing engine No 9754 was built in 1904 with sister engine No 9755 and sold to the Marquis de Castello, Melor. These engines were fitted with two ploughing speeds working on the one upright shaft. These official works photographs show both sides of No 9755 and were taken prior to entering the paint shop. *(courtesy Institute of Agricultural History)*

173.   Fowler Class B4 compound ploughing engine either No 9896 *Joan* or No 9897 *Darby*, Registration Nos PB9668 and PB9667. They were built in June 1904 and sold to Alfred J. Ward & Sons of Egham, Surrey where they spent all their working lives. In 1952 they were sold to J.W. Hardwick & Sons of West Ewell who presumably cut them up.   *(author's collection)*

174.   Fowler Class B4 compound ploughing engine No 10252 was built in June 1910 with sister engine No 10253. They were fitted with double speed ploughing gear and delivered to Dynes Bros of Cardington, Beds where they received the Registration Nos NM272 and NM273. In August 1934 they were sold to C.W. Johnson of Bygrave, Herts, who in the same year either sold or traded them to dealer George Taylor of Redbourn, Herts. They were then sold in 1936 to Herbert Hailey of Great Wymondley, Herts who worked them until 1940 when they went to Reginald G. Kendal of Biggleswade, Beds. This photograph was taken shortly after delivery to Dynes Bros.   *(courtesy Major Ind/RLS)*

175.   Fowler Class Z4 compound ploughing engine No 10316 was built in 1908 with sister engine No 10317 and sent to Fowler's depot in Magdeburg, Germany. This works photograph shows her undergoing steam trials before entering the paint shop.   *(courtesy Institute of Agricultural History)*

176.   A new Fowler 14nhp boiler No 10334 supplied to T.B. Kitchener of Potton, Beds on 10th February 1905 for fitting in their engine No 2705 which they had bought new with sister engine No 2706 in September 1875. They later carried the Registration Nos NM210 and NM211.   *(courtesy Institute of Agricultural History)*

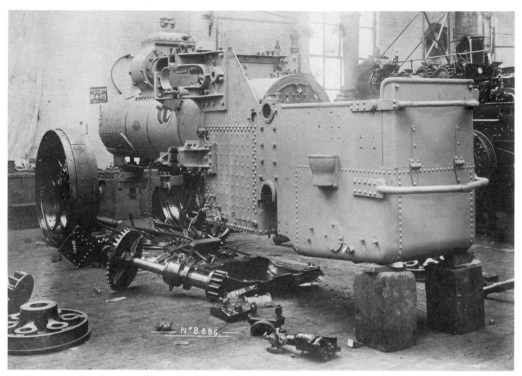

177/178. Fowler Class AA2 compound ploughing engine No 10403 *Ernesto* was built in 1906 with sister engine No 10402 and sold abroad to E. Ayulo & Co. These official works photographs show her during assembly in grey undercoat and with various components displayed around her.

(courtesy Institute of Agricultural History)

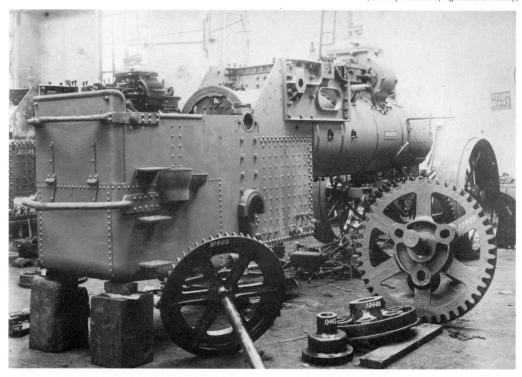

Fowler Class B4 compound ploughing engines Nos 10944 and 10945, Registration Nos EW2188 and EW2189, were built in March 1907 and sold to Gotobed & Smith of Somersham, Hunts. They are recorded as being for sale in 1936 and by 1943 were owned by H. Gingell of Horningsea, Cambs. Later they passed to C. Kidman of Biggleswade, Beds where they were photographed in May 1957 shortly before being cut up.

79.   Fowler No 10944.
(Author's collection)

80.   Nos 10945 and 10944.
(Author's collection)

81.   Fowler No 10945.
(Author's collection)

182. Fowler Class AA4 compound ploughing engine No 11654 was built in 1909 with sister engine 11655 and delivered to the Magdeburg Branch in Germany along with four other pairs built in this batch.

(author's collection)

183. Fowler Class B4 compound ploughing engine No 12242 was built in 1910 with sister engine 12243. They were fitted with two speed ploughing gear and sold to Richardson & Wakelin of Witham, Essex who named them *Vulcan* and *Trojan*. In March 1918 they were sold to Mitchell & Learmonth of Wix, Essex where this photograph was taken on 24th September 1919; whilst in their ownership they received the Registration Nos NO575 and NO576. Their next owner was J. Copping & Sons of Great Bentley, Essex but by June 1940 they had been sold to Arthur Baldock of Haverhill in West Suffolk where they spent the rest of their working lives.

(courtesy Major Ind/RLS)

184/185. Fowler Class B4 compound ploughing engines No 12646 *Surprise* and No 12647 *Dreadnought* were built in December 1910 and sold to A. & P. Coates Ltd of Windridge, Herts. On a date not recorded they were bought by P.C. Kidman of Biggleswade, Beds. Their last owner was George Taylor, engine dealer of Redbourn, Herts who presumably cut them up. These two photographs were taken just outside St Albans in 1919. The top photograph shows No 12646 with driver W. Pratley whilst the lower illustration shows No 12647 with driver J.G. Pratley. *(author's collection)*

186. Fowler Class T1 compound double drum ploughing engine No 12958 was built in 1911 and delivered to the Magdeburg Branch for a customer in Germany.

(author's collection)

187. Fowler medium cultivator with rigid tines and four point lifting gear. This is implement No 11110 photographed in the works yard in December 1913.

(author's collection)

188. Fowler Class K7 compound ploughing engine No 13400, Registration No KE5858, was built in 1913 with sister engine No 13399, Registration No KE5857 and sold to William Blacklock of Lydd, Kent, where they spent all of their working lives before being cut up for scrap in April 1950.

(author's collection)

189.   Fowler No 13473.   (courtesy F.H. Gillford)

Fowler Class BB compound ploughing engines Nos 13473 and 13474 were built in June 1913, fitted with double speed ploughing gear and sold to Briggs & Son of Stamford, Kesteven. They became Nos 11 and 12 in their fleet of engines and later acquired the Registration Nos CT4287 and CT4288. When Briggs & Son had finished with them No 13473 was sold to Bath & Portland Stone Firms Ltd whilst No 13474 went to Herbert V. Williams of Chippenham, Wilts.   (courtesy F.H. Gillford))

190.   Fowler No 13474.   (courtesy F.H. Gillford)

191. Fowler Class BB compound ploughing engine No 13784 was built circa 191[ ] with sister engine No 13785 and delivered to the Magdeburg Branch in Germany. Fowlers built ten pairs of engines in this batch Nos 13776 to 13785, the last two pairs going to Germany.
(author's collection)

192. Fowler Class AA compound ploughing engine No 13794 *Kitchener*, Registration No BD5560 was built in August 1916 with sister engine 13795 *Jellicoe*, Registration No BD5556, and sold to John Jellis of Titchmarsh, Northants, where they spent all of their workin[g] lives. This photograph taken 1937 shows *Kitchener* cultivating near Thrapston, Northants.
(author's collection)

193. This photograph taken April 1956 shows engines Nos 13794 *Kitchener* and 137[ ] *Jellicoe* sitting derelict in the yard at Titchmarsh; they had last been licenced in 1942.
(author's collection)

94. Fowler Class BKS compound ploughing engine No 13952 was built in March 1914 with sister engine No 13953 and was fitted with two speed ploughing gear. Both engines were sold to F.J. Hunt of Guilden Morden, Cambs, where they received the registration Nos CE7853 and CE7852. In August 1935 they were sold to W. Cranwell of Varishall, Essex who used them until early in the war as by November 1941 they were owned by the Essex War Agricultural Executive Committee.
(Courtesy C. Roads)

95. Fowler Class BKS compound ploughing engines Nos 13956 and 13957, Registration Nos CE7855 and CE7854, were built in July 1916 and sold to F.J. Hunt of Guilden Morden, in Cambridgeshire. In August 1935 they were sold to George Taylor, the well known engine dealer of Redbourn, Herts, who in turn sold them to R.G. Kendall of Biggleswade, Beds. In 1945 they sold No 13957 to H. Howitt of Stotfold, Beds where she was used to steam greenhouses. No 13956 was sold for scrap in 1953. This photograph was taken in Taylor's yard at Redbourn on 22nd June 1936.
(Courtesy R.G. Pratt)

96. Fowler Class AA6 compound ploughing engines Nos 13982 *Southend* and 13983 *Tilbury*, Registration Nos NO690 and NO691, were built in May 1915 and sold to Charles H. Hockley Ltd of Hatfield Broad Oak, Essex. They later became the property of John Patten of Little Hadham, Herts their last recorded owner. This photograph, taken on 14th October 1935, shows the pair on the road with *Tilbury* taking the plough and *Southend* following with the sleeping van and watercart.
(Courtesy R.G. Pratt)

197. Fowler two-wheel water cart
No 13978 fitted with Bodans No 5 size hand
pump photographed in the works yard in
July 1922.
(author's collection)

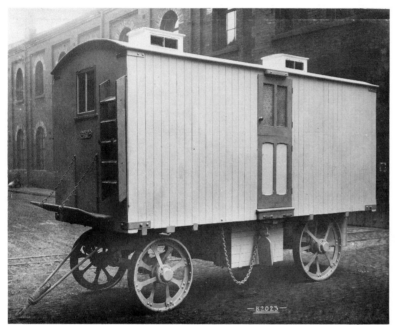

198. Fowler five berth sleeping van
No 13685 'English type' for ploughing
tackle, photographed at Fowler's Works in
March 1920.
(author's collection)

199. Fowler Class BB compound
ploughing engine No 14186 was built in
April 1914 and fitted with double speed
ploughing gear. With sister engine
No 14185 she was sold to Richardson &
Wakelin of Witham, Essex who gave them
the names *Hercules* and *Achilles*. In March
1918 they were sold to the Witham Steam
Plough Co, (AC Mens), where they received
the Registration Nos NO693 and NO692.
They were later sold to R. Copping & Sons
of Blackheath, Essex. They were advertised
for sale in 1949, No 14186 being sold to the
Essex Steam Rolling Association of
Kelvedon.
(courtesy R.G. Pratt)

200.   Fowler No 14269 ■ at work when owned by A.H. Tebbutt.   *(author's collection)*

Fowler Class BBS compound ploughing engine No 14269 ■, Registration No NO750, was built in August 1914 with sister engine No 14268 ■ and fitted with piston valves and two speed ploughing gear. They were sold to Robert Hilder of Takely, Essex and were later purchased by Albert H. Tebbutt of Rickling, in Essex. In 1936 they became the property of Bomford & Evershed of Salford Priors in Warwickshire. Twenty years later the firm became Bomford & Carr of Binton and then Bomford and Wilkinson.

201.   No 14269 ■ on the road whilst in the ownership of Bomford & Evershed: she is fitted with a tail rope winding drum and is towing a trailer containing a dredging scoop, a living van and watercart.

(courtesy R. Smith)

202. Fowler Class BBS compound ploughing engines Nos 14270 and 14271, Registration Nos DO2070 and DO2069, were built in September 1916. They were fitted with Firth's valve gear and sold to George Cauldwell of Weston, Holland (Lincs). In 1924 they were sold to L.F. Briggs & Son of Stamford, No 14271 later going to Beeby Bros of Rempstone. This photograph was taken at Cauldwell's yard in 1934.

(courtesy F.H. Gillford)

203. Fowler Class BBS compound ploughing engine No 14273 was built in May 1917 with sister engine No 14272, Registration Nos DO1924 and DO1923. They were fitted with double speed ploughing gear and sold to W. Dennis & Son of Kirton, Holland (Lincs) where they spent all of their working lives, being last licenced in 1938. This photograph was taken on 27th October 1926 at Kirton and shows a Fowler reversible disc harrow on test.

(courtesy Institute of Agricultural History)

204. Fowler Class BB ploughing engines Nos 14351 *King George V* (left) and 14352 *King Albert* (right) were built in February 1916 and sold to George F. Townsend of Exning in West Suffolk. In March 1919 they were sold through George Thurlow, engine dealers of Stowmarket (who are still in business), to the Sutton Scotney Steam Ploughing Company in Hampshire where they received the Registration Nos HO5798 and HO5799. In May 1935 Thurlow's took them back and sold them to John Turney & Company of Weston on the Green in Oxfordshire. They changed hands once again in August 1940 when acquired by Thomas T. Boughton & Sons of Amersham, Bucks who worked them until November 1947 when he sold them to their final owner, H.V. Smith & Son of Tottenham, Middlesex. This photograph shows them during their period with John Turney en route to a dredging job. *(courtesy R.G. Pratt)*

205. Fowler Class BB1 compound ploughing engine No 14383 ■ *Prince*, Registration No NM1284, was built in August 1917 with sister engine No 14384 ■ *Princess*, Registration No NM1283, and sold to Benjamin Howkins of Bromham, Beds. By July 1924 they were in the ownership of the well known steam ploughing contractor John Patten of Much Hadham, Herts where they worked until the firm was sold up in June 1960. This photograph was taken just before the firm ceased operating. *(author's collection)*

206. No 14708 in Smith's yard at Wymington in 1956.
(author's collection)

Fowler Class BB compound ploughing engines Nos 14708 and 14709, Registration Nos NM303 and NM304, were built in November 1917 and sold to Sir A.E. Bowen of Sharnbrook, Beds. In 1926 they went to Harris & Measures of Bletsoe, Beds who worked them for ten years before selling them, in 1936, to Ralph Savage, a ploughing contractor of Riseley, Beds.

In 1949 Savage sold them to William W. Smith of Wymington, Beds where 14709 was cut up in error by the scrapman who attempted to make good his mistake by supplying Oxford Steam Ploughing Co engine No 75, Registration No BD5585, as a replacement. Within a few years this odd pair were also cut up.

207. No 14708 and No 75 in Smith's yard at Wymington in 1956.
(author's collection)

208. No 14709 photographed on the road at Newton Bromswold.
(courtesy F.H. Gillford)

102

209. Fowler Class AA compound ploughing engine No 14727 ■ was built in October 1918 with sister engine No 14726 ■ and sold to Lewis Jackson of Toppesfield, Essex where this photograph was taken on 30th May 1924.
(courtesy Major Ind/RLS)

210. Fowler K7 compound ploughing engine No 14734, Registration No CJ4208, was built in 1918 and sold to John Read of Haywood, Hereford along with sister engine No 14735, Registration No CJ4207. They eventually finished their working lives with Ivor E. Probert of Burghill, Hereford. At some time in the thirties while in the ownership of John Read she went out of control on the outskirts of Hereford and mounted a grass bank before overturning and assuming this rather undignified position.
(courtesy John Haining)

211. Fowler Class BB1 compound ploughing engine No 15143 ■, Registration No BP6127 was built in March 1918 with sister engine No 15142 ■, Registration No BP6125 and sold to John Sparks of Yapton, West Sussex. As the result of a court case, they were ordered to be sold along with other engines and plant. The sale took place on Tuesday, 7th October 1924, the auctioneers being Messrs Harry as. Burt of Steyning and Messrs Stride and Son of Chichester. This pair of engines, a 13-tine cultivator, six-furrow plough, seven-ring presser, two-wheel watercart and a Fowler sleeping van were bought by W.J. Overland of Wangford, East Suffolk and at a later date became the property of George Thurlow & Sons of Stowmarket. In 1932 they sold 15143 ■ to J. Collins of Dormston, Worcs who paired her with No 15175 ■, Registration No AD8664, which he had bought from G.W. Stephens of Hinton, Worcs. This latter pair are illustrated at Inkberrow, Worcs in August 1958 with 15143 ■ nearest to the camera.
(author's collection)

212. Fowler Class BB1 compound ploughing engine No 15163■, Registration No WR7151, was built in May 1918 with sister engine No 15162, Registration No WR7150, and sold to George Gunter of Wetherby in the West Riding of Yorkshire. By 1923 they had gone to Cole Bros of Sleaford, Lincs who sold them in 1927 to How Bros of Leighton, Hunts. After this they went to E.A. Warth of Ellington, Hunts before being sold to H.J. Roads of Caxton, Cambs. This photograph, taken in August 1959, shows her ploughing at Orwell, Cambs.
(author's collection)

213. Fowler Class BB1 compound ploughing engine No 15180, Registration No PB9666, was built in June 191? with sister engine No 15181, Registration No PB9665 for the Ministry of Agriculture and Fisheries and sold to Alfred J. Ward & Sons of Egham, Surrey. In 1950 they were sold to F. Goymer & Sons of Barking, Essex from where it is believed they were exported to India. The photograph shows her cultivating whilst in the ownership of Alfred J. Ward & Sons.
(author's collection)

214. A Fowler Class BB1 compound ploughing engine, either No 15192 or 15193, Registration Nos CT4345 and CT4347, built in July 1918 and sold via the Ministry of Agriculture and Fisheries to Edward Morley of Grantham. By December 1943 they had been sold to the Pipewell Ploughing Company in Northants and in 1953 they were purchased by G.L. Swan of Doncaster, their last recorded owner.
(courtesy F.H. Gillford)

15. Fowler Class AA7 compound ploughing engine No 15233 was built in December 1917 with sister engine No 15232 and received the Registration Nos EW2191 and EW2190. They were sold via the Ministry of Agriculture and Fisheries to W.H. Gotobed & Son, Somersham, Hunts. In 1936 they where sold to E. Deamer & Son of Hardwick, Cambridgeshire and on 8th August 1941 became the property of the Cambridgeshire War Agricultural Executive Committee.
(courtesy C. Roads)

16. Fowler Class BB1 compound ploughing engine No 15418 was built in July 1919 with sister engine No 15419. They carried the registration Nos BH6813 and BH6814 and were sold to Sir Herbert Leon at Bletchley Park, Bucks. Later they were purchased by John Turney & Co of Weston on the Green in Oxfordshire. In March 1948 they were advertised for sale and were bought by Thomas T. Boughton & Sons of Amersham Common, their last recorded owner.
(courtesy C. Roads)

17. Fowler Class BB1 compound ploughing engines Nos 15426■ and 15427■, Registration Nos WR7181 and WR7182, were built in July 1920 and sold to Kitching & Sons of Sykehouse, West Riding but moved with their owners down to Ealand, Lindsey in 1921. Later they were sold to C. Vamplew & Sons of Grimoldby, Lindsey and in May 1947 they were bought by J.K. Gandy of Thurlby, Kesteven. This photograph was taken in April 1958 when the engines were parked on the side of the Stamford to Bourne road.
(author's collection)

218. *Victory* (above) drawing the cultivator and water cart and *Dreadnought* following with the living van, passing West Wratting Drove on 23rd September 1949 whilst owned by Arthur Baldock.
(courtesy A.C. Durrant)

Fowler Class BB compound ploughing engine No 15451■ *Victory*, Registration No SD9378, was built in March 1925 with sister engine No 15452■ *Dreadnought*, Registration No SD9377 and sold to the Orchard Sugar Refining Company Ltd, of Greenock, Scotland. By March 1937 they had moved south into the ownership of Arthur M. Cole of Sleaford, Lincs and were later sold to Arthur Baldock of Haverhill, West Suffolk from where H.J. Road of Orwell, Cambs bought them in 1952.

219. *Victory* (left) cultivating at Orwell in August 1955 with driver Roads on the footplate.
(author's collection)

220. Fowler Class Z7 compound ploughing engine No 16719 was built in July 1926 with sister engine No 16720, Registration Nos MK7541 and MK7542, and so to Concrete Aggregates Ltd of Chiswick, Middlesex. In 1934 they were bought by Bomford & Evershed of Salford Priors, Warwickshire where they received the Registration Nos WD8709 and WD7831. Engine No 16720 was last licenced in March 1950 and cut up some time after that. No 16719 was sold possibly around the same time to Lunnicks of Reading, fitted with a crane and exported to Tasmania.
This photograph shows 16719 ploughing at Rye, Sussex in September 1937.
(author's collection)

221. A Fowler B4 compound ploughing engine with 6/7 furrow 'English type' plough, on test at Leeds in July 1912.
(author's collection)

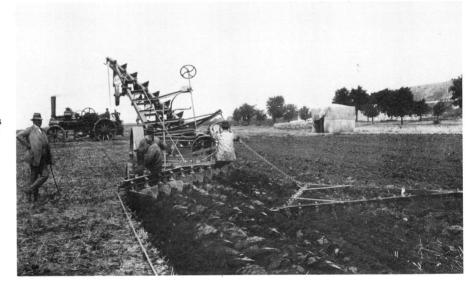

22. A Fowler ten-furrow plough and harrow at work in Germany. This photograph was received at the Leeds Works in January 1913.
(author's collection)

223. Fowler seven-furrow bevel frame patent anti-balance disc plough No 14274 on test at Leeds in September 1923.
(author's collection)

224/225. The first Garrett Suffolk Punch tractor No 32974, Registration No BJ3345 was built in 1917 and photographed whilst giving one of the many demonstrations that were staged before she was sold to S.J. Brown of Naas in Co. Kildare, Southern Ireland.
(courtesy J.L. Middlemiss and J. Hair)

The events of the First World War not only speeded up the development of the internal combustion engine, but also made available large markets which would have been very much slower in opening up had it not been for wartime demand. Richard Garrett & Sons Ltd of Leiston saw the need for a steam version of the internal combustion tractor that was becoming available in ever-increasing numbers. In 1917 they produced their first Agri-Motor or the 'Suffolk Punch' as the type became known and after a series of demonstrations she was sold 1918. Others followed but they were not a success, their weight, operating costs and, above all, the trouble in raising steam compared with the ease of starting the petrol engine were all factors against them. In the end only eight were built, the last two being sold abroad to the Sena Sugar Estates Ltd of Mopea Chinde.

226. Garrett Suffolk Punch No 33180■, Registration No BJ4483, was built in July 191■ and sold to John Goddard of Tunstall, East Suffolk.
(courtesy R.G. Pratt)

227. The 1870 Howard portable engine with the windlass driven by a shaft connected to the end of the crankshaft by means of a universal joint, the other end similarly fixed to the shaft of the windlass. In this photograph the driver is seen guiding the rope onto the drum with a wooden rake to assist uniform coiling.
(courtesy Institute of Agricultural History)

228. The Howard belt driven windlass of 1874; combined with an ordinary portable engine, provided a simple and effective set of roundabout ploughing tackle. The engine and windlass were joined by a single bolt for the convenience of moving from field to field.
(courtesy Institute of Agricultural History)

229. Howard two cylinder three-wheel ploughing engine built circa 1864 at the Britannia Iron Works in Bedford. Fitted with two winding drums, it was intended for the double engine system.

(courtesy Institute of Agricultural History)

230. The Improved Howard two cylinder three-wheel ploughing engine of 1867 which was exhibited at the Paris Exhibition in that year. Coal was carried in the tender over the water tank but it would seem that the fire hole door was only accessible from the ground, a considerable inconvenience when travelling on the road.

(courtesy Institute of Agricultural History)

1. Howard 8nhp single cylinder ploughing engine built in 1877 and exhibited on their stand at the Royal Show at Liverpool that year. She was bought off the stand by Mr Stephenson of Burwell, Cambs where she worked for the next fifty-one years. In 1928 she was bought back by Howards to put on display at their works and in this photograph taken by Mr Paige Stuart of Bedford she is seen leaving Burwell at the start of her four-day journey to Bedford which she accomplished without any trouble. Alas she was cut up when the firm crashed in the 1929-1930 slump. *(Author's collection)*

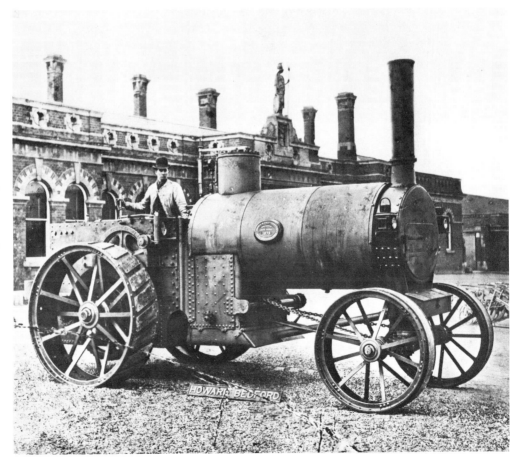

2. The first Howard design of single cylinder four wheeled ploughing engine built in 1873, standing at the front of Britannia Iron Works, Bedford. This picture shows her in traction engine form, without the ploughing gear being fitted. The steering on the earlier engines was by a vertical shaft on the top of which was fixed the steering wheel, on the bottom end was a worm turning a sprocket mounted on a stub shaft which connected by means of a pitch chain to the ordinary chain roller fitted to the firebox. *(Courtesy J. Haining)*

233. In 1873 Howards built their first four-wheel 12nhp ploughing engine which was exhibited on their stand at The Royal Show in Bedford the following year. By 1875 certain modifications had been made and it was available also as an 8nhp or 16nhp engine. Unlike the first design which featured a vertical steering arrangement this was now by a slanting shaft and worm onto the chain roller; known as the 'Farmers Engine' it was shown at the Taunton Show that year. The ploughing gear which was carried on a detachable frame could be removed to enable the engine to perform the normal duties of a traction engine without the burden of carrying the extra weight of the ploughing equipment. The rear end view (above) shows two winding drums which permitted double engine working opposite a moving anchor, or on the roundabout system.

(author's collection)

234. A gear side view of the Howard 'Farmers Engine' at work.
(author's collection)

235. The Howard 6nhp single cylinder ploughing engine introduced at the Kilburn Agriculture Show in 1879. Various modifications were introduced, the most noticeable being the placing of the flywheel on the right hand side of the engine and a handsome dome cover reminiscent of those fitted to the locomotives of the Midland Railway which ran alongside the Britannia Works. This and the picture overleaf show the engine belonging to Reuben Haybittle of Ottershaw, Surrey with the ploughing gear removed.

(courtesy B.D. Stoyel)

236. Another view of the Howard at Ottershaw, Surrey.

237.   Manns ploughing engine, number unknown, designed by Parmiter of Tisbury, Wiltshire and built for him circa 1899 by Manns Patent Steam Wagon Co of Leeds. It was intended for both direct traction cultivating and for the roundabout system. The rear wheel was in the form of a 'V' straked roller, whose axle extended on either side and on which were mounted the winding drums when required for cable cultivating. The drive to the roller was disengaged to enable the drums to rotate, alternately winding in and unwinding the cable. It would appear that the spark arrester on the chimney has been drawn onto the print in ink as it is out of contrast with the rest of the photograph and was probably added for illustrating a catalogue for the overseas market. It is quite possible that this was the only example built, and is shown set up for roundabout cultivating with the implement in the background.   (author's collection)

238/239.   Marshall 6nhp single cylinder ploughing engine No 6071 was built in June 1878 as a special order for Thomas Lewis of Lyonshall, Kington, Herefordshire. This was a standard 6nhp traction engine with the front axle extended forward to enable a horizontal winding drum to be fitted beneath the boiler. After the death of Mr Lewis in 1894 she was bought by Mr Williams of Woonton, a nearby village and stayed there for a number of years during which time the ploughing gear was removed. Her next owner was Mr Gwyn Price of Pentre Jack, Hereford where she received the Registration No CJ4649, was fitted with a cab and used for threshing. Eventually the rear wheels wore out and were replaced with an old pair of McLaren traction engine wheels and in this condition she became the property of Mr S.M. Price of Llowes, Radnor where she was used for a number of years before she was left at his brother's place at Pentre Jack until sold for scrap circa 1955. Illustrated above in original condition, the picture below shows the changes made over the years: the ploughing gear removed, the remains of the cab, now all but gone, and the McLaren wheels fitted to the rear; the driver is Mr S.M. Price with his father behind him, the flagman is a Mr John Pugh.

(both photographs courtesy R. Smith)

240/241/242. J. & H. MacLar[en]
8nhp traction engine No 112[?]
was built in July 1881 and so[ld]
to John Piddlesden of
Aldington, Kent. Later she w[as]
sold to E. Checksfield of
Burmarsh, Kent, where she
received the Registration No
KL2176. In 1961 she was sol[d]
into preservation.

These three photographs sho[w]
a set of roundabout tackle at
work using a four-furrow
plough on the Romney Marsh
in Kent in the early thirties.
By this method the engine
drove a windlass consisting o[f]
two drums revolving in
opposite directions, as one
drum wound in the wire rope
the other played it out. The
rope was then led around the
field on pulleys before being
attached to the plough. As
work progressed so the pulle[y]
would be moved up the field[.]
Although a lot cheaper in
capital outlay it never proved
as popular as the two engine
system.

(author's collection)

43. One end of the drive shaft is fitted to the windlass via a universal joint. The other end of this shaft fits inside a box shaft to allow for a varying distance between the engine and windlass. The box shaft is then fitted to the special hub of the flywheel by means of another universal joint.
(Author's collection)

The photographs on this page are really outside the scope of this book as they show McLaren 112■ in preservation. It is felt justified to include them as they show in detail much that cannot be seen in the existing old photographs of roundabout ploughing tackle at work.

44. A close up view of Fowler windlass No 8024. The drive shaft can be seen with one end fitted to a universal joint, the other within the box shaft.
(Author's collection)

45. This view shows the windlass chained front and rear to the engine and the windlass clutch lever extended to be within reach of the driver.
(Author's collection)

246/247/248. McLaren 12nhp compound engine No 1541■, Registration No HO5832, was built in October 1918 with sister engine No 1540, Registration No HO5831 and sold to Lt. Col. Miles R.F. Courage of Sutton Scotney, Wiltshire. On dates not recorded they were sold to F. White of Crowdhill, Hants, then to F.J. Honour of Northleach Glos, and finally to their last commercial owner William H. Whitley of Welstor, Asburton, Devon 1540 finished her days in a barn opposite the home of William Whitley at Barton Pines, near Paignton, Devon where the author photographed her in September 1955, three years later she was cut up where she stood. After being separated from her sister engine 1541■ was used to haul loads of timber chained together up the sides of a steep valley, a standard Fordson tractor being used to return the wire rope ready for the next pull. On one occasion the site of the tree felling was not visible to the driver of the engine so the operations were conducted by William Whitley astride his hunter using his hunting horn. (It is tempting to picture him resplendent in his hunting pink but I feel this is taxing one's imagination too much!) Eventually the engine was laid aside at Welstor until located by the author who purchased her from Noyce of Kingsbridge, a scrap dealer who had bought her to cut up only the previous week.

These three photographs show her just after arrival from Devon at Gowers Works, Bedford where she went for examination prior to her first steaming.

(author's collection)

249/250.   J. & H. Maclaren 16nhp compound ploughing engines Nos 1550 and 1551 were built in May 1918 and sold to Benjamin Howkins of Bromham, Beds. In 1920 he sold them to A.T. Oliver & Sons of Wandon End, Herts where they received the Registration Nos NK933 and NK936 and spent the rest of their working lives. These two photographs show them cultivating for A.T. Oliver & Sons: (above) right hand engine No 1550 and (below) left hand engine No 1551.   *(courtesy Steam Plough Club)*

251.   J. & H. McLaren 14nhp single cylinder ploughing engine No 15 pictured on 26th June 1915. Built in May 1878 with sister engine No 16 they were sold to Archibald Ainslie of Dodridge, Midlothian. They were then bought circa 1911 by dealer William Reynolds of Bedford who sold them in 1911 to Thomas Stovin of Welton, Lincolnshire, their last recorded owner, where they received the Registration Nos BE7989 and BE7990.   (courtesy Major Ind/RLS)

252.   J. & H. McLaren 16nhp compound ploughing engines Nos 1555 and 1554, Registration Nos BJ6875 and BJ6874, were built in June 1919 and sold to the Marquess of Grantham at Easton Park, East Suffolk. They later went to I.C. Sturgeon of Aldham, West Suffolk where they received the new Registration Nos CF4193 and CF4195. They were photographed at the sale on 18th June 1933 when purchased by B.W. Death, of Lavenham, West Suffolk. Their next owner was Mr A.E. Davies of Aldham Hall, followed by Francis Mortlock of Lavenham, West Suffolk.   (courtesy R.G. Pratt)

253/254. Single cylinder ploughing engine belonging to the Oxfordshire Steam Ploughing Company of Cowley after running away downhill and turning over at Fossebridge, near Northleach in March 1914. Both the driver and steersman were able to leap clear and avoid injury. *(both photographs courtesy R. Smith)*

255. A 1919 photograph of one the Oxford Steam Plough Company's No 1 set, a piston valve single cylinder ploughing engine, either No 41 or 42, built by the company circa 1909. In 1920 they were sold, the records are not complete but the owner was either Bailey and Keen of Eakring or A.T. Loyd of Lockinge.

(courtesy R. Smith)

256. Oxford Steam Ploughing Company 12nhp compound ploughing engine No 56, Registration No BW4611, Fleet No 230, standing in Allens Yard at Cowley. Together with her sister engine No 55, Registration No BW4610, Fleet No 247, they were the company's No 3 set. *(author's collection)*

257/258. An Oxford Steam Ploughing Company 10nhp single cylinder engine, it is either No 73 or sister engine No 74, Registration Nos BW4008 or BW4009. These were Fowler single cylinder engines rebuilt with the company's own design of boiler, cylinder block, piston valves and safety valves and were their No 2 set. These photographs show one of the engines at work whilst owned by J.E. Whiting of Castlethorpe, Northants who bought them in 1934. They were cut up in 1947.
(author's collection)

259. Ransomes, Sims & Jefferies 8nhp single cylinder traction engine No 14086 (below), built in December 1901 and sold to the Darby Digger Company where she was fitted with a chain driven rotary digger and exhibited at the Smithfield Show in that year. She then went to Phillips & Dowsett of Southend on Sea, whether on trial or firm sale is not recorded but it was eventually returned to the Darby Digger Company circa 1906/7. She was sold to F.G. Keeling of Crays Hill, Essex where she was last licenced in 1923.
(courtesy Steam Plough Club)

260/261/262. These very old but rare, photographs show a Savage 10nhp 'Agriculturist' engine at work ploughing on the roundabout system. This was in fact a traction engine adapted for ploughing for which it was necessary to first jack up the engine so that the rear wheels were free to revolve. The centre tyres on each wheel had then to be removed, revealing the winding drum in the centre of each one. If you were lucky enough to be working on hard ground you could be set ready to be working in ten minutes, but if the ground was soft it could take twice as long. When the engine was ready a rope was led off from each of the rear wheels, one forward and around pulleys to the plough and one from the rear of the engine around pulleys to the other end of the plough. Then as the engine revolved its wheels one unwound the cable whilst the other wound in and the plough travelled up and down the field in a line parallel to the engine. Of the four pulleys used the two opposite each end of the plough were in fact Savages Patent Automatic Anchors, not only serving as pulleys but automatically moving up each side of the field towards the engine as work progressed. A complete set of tackle consisted of one 'Agriculturist' engine, one Savage's Improved Steam Plough and Digger, two Patent Automatic Anchors, three large safety snatch blocks (pulleys) and three three-wheeled rope porters (these kept the rope off the ground as much as possible to prevent undue wear). Three men were required to operate the system, one each on the engine and plough and the other to tend to the rope around the edges of the field.
(courtesy J.L. Middlemiss)

263. Savory double cylinder ploughing engine built in July 1861.The cylinders are located beneath the smokebox, drive to the drum being by means of a pinion on the crankshaft engaging teeth on the inside end of the drum. The large drum of six feet diameter was necessary to accommodate the ploughing rope which in the early years was made of wrought iron and would not stand up to the sharper bends of a small drum.

(author's collection)

264. The second design of Savory ploughing engine built in 1864, double cylinder but now with the chimney at the driver's end. The first pair were sold to Benjamin Bomford of Pitchill, Warks who is thought to be the gentleman sitting in the tender observing his new engines at work. *(author's collection)*

265/266. Built by the firm of Yorkshire enginee[r] Summerscales Ltd of Phoenix Foundry, Keighley, t[he] Summerscales steam tractor is shown during trials September 1918. She was fitted with a four cylinder '[V'] engine which was totally enclosed and developed 25b[hp] working on superheated steam supplied at 200lb per [sq.] inch (14.06kgf/cm^2) and was designed to pull a 4 furr[ow] plough over uncultivated moorland. When the design w[as] planned war time conditions and the use of home produc[ed] fuel no doubt influenced the choice of steam power, but t[he] war was drawing towards it's end and yet they st[ill] proceeded with steam despite the large number of petr[ol] tractors which had come from the U.S.A. to help the w[ar] effort and which had so convincingly proved the[ir] superiority. They thought that the English farmer was mo[re] familiar with steam and would prefer it to the mo[re] complicated internal combustion engine. The *Commerci[al] News* of 12th September 1918, reporting the first tests [of] the tractor said, 'The only land available at the time was [a] piece of uncultivated moorland, on which heather, wi[th] stems and roots like whipcord was growing, yet even wi[th] a four furrow plough and plain coulters the tractor nev[er] hesitated. In fact the few engineers privileged to see t[he] tractor at work were unanimous in proclaiming it "a litt[le] marvel".' This contrasts with the following report: February 1921 Sam Rollinson of East Ardsley, nr Barnsle[y] bought a tractor which received the Registration N[o.] WR7349. It was licensed again in 1923 but a few years la[ter] an enquiry from the licensing authority brought the answ[er] from Mr Rollinson that the tractor was useless and certain[ly] would not be used again.

(Left: courtesy T.B. Paisley, below: courtesy J.L. Middlemiss)

267.   Wallis & Steevens 4¼ ton compound Oilbath tractor No 2854 fitted with two-way ploughing gear undergoing trials at the Whiteditch Field, Sherbourne Road, Basingstoke in 1906. She was built in September 1906 and sold to Richard B. Harvey of Shalbourne, Isle of Wight but was later returned to the manufacturers. By 1929 she had been sold to Thomas Guy of Newport, I.O.W. where she received the Registration No DL4649. Her last owner was W. Matthews & Sons, also of Newport.   *(courtesy R. Smith)*

268.   Wallis & Steevens 4¼ ton compound Oilbath tractor No 2923 was built in July 1907 and fitted with two way ploughing gear. She was sold to H. Berry of Whitchurch, Hants.   *(author's collection)*

269. Official photograph of Wallis & Steevens 4¾ ton compound Oilbath tractor No 7327 at work cultivating. She was built in January 1913, fitted with attachments for direct ploughing and was sold to Mrs S.A. Butler of Cliddesden, Hants.

(author's collection)

270. Yarrow & Hilditch double cylinder ploughing engine built in 1862 by Mr Coleman, an agricultural engineer of Chelmsford, Essex. At the time this engine was designed Yarrow was aged 18 and Hilditch 17!

(author's collection)